ABOUT ALCOHOLISM: A COMMON SENSE PERSPECTIVE

3

ABOUT ALCOHOLISM:

A COMMON SENSE PERSPECTIVE

Donald A. Staccia, Ph.D.

Acosep Corporation
Publishing Division
401 N. Plum St.
Springfield, Ohio 45504

ISBN 0-9616402-0-0 (Cloth)
ISBN 0-9616402-1-9 (Paper)

Printed in the United States of America

DEDICATION
This book has a two part dedication

First

It is dedicated to the memory of my loving mother

Blanche Conley Staccia
December 2, 1914 — August 26, 1982

and

John Victor Staccia
Her dedicated husband of thirty six years.

Second

It is dedicated to my family

Joyce A. Staccia, my ex-wife and best friend.

OUR CHILDREN

Donald A. Staccia (28) and Leslie H. Staccia (30), my *pregnant* daughter-in-law, and first grandchild-to-be.

Don is an electrical engineer who is now a corporate executive.

Christina A. Staccia (26), graduate student at Ohio State University.

Gregory A. Staccia (24), Ex-Navy and a free spirited young man.

Angela A. Staccia (22), graduate student at Wright State University.

CONTENTS

INTRODUCTION

About Alcoholism: A Common Sense Perspective is a book written for all those who suffer from alcoholism. It is for not only the drinking person, but also those who suffer with him. This includes the alcoholic's spouse, children, parents, sisters, brothers, grandparents, extended relatives, employer, employees, friends and neighbors. These persons are commonly referred to as "significant others" and number in the tens of millions.

It is estimated that for every alcoholic, at least five significant others are involved in his suffering. In fact, many significant others often suffer even more than the alcoholic. If you are an alcoholic, a significant other, suspect you have a drinking problem of any kind or are just interested in the subject, then this book is for you.

This book is unique because it reflects my global background in alcoholism, i.e., victim, scholar, researcher, educator, clinician and author. My background as a victim of alcoholism includes being born of an alcoholic parent, drinking at age thirteen, and becoming an alcoholic by fifteen. At age sixteen, I went to work in a factory to help support my family and joined the Armed Forces on my seventeenth birthday.

In 1966, after twelve years of service and a veteran of Korea and Vietnam, I was "kicked out" of the military due to alcoholism. After eight more years of alcoholism complications, I hit bottom in 1974. At that time, I was suicidal, divorced, jobless, had a Bad Conduct

Discharge from the military and only an eighth grade formal education.

My recovery is inspirational. Since starting recovery in 1974, most of my life has been dedicated to a career of helping other alcoholics and their families recover. This career began as a volunteer counselor in a halfway house for alcoholics. It now includes clinical experience with treating the alcoholic and his family in many and varied settings which include two acute care hospitals, a university counseling center, and the Ohio State Rehabilitation Services Commission. Today, I am a recognized authority on alcoholism and recovery.

My doctoral thesis, based on an original and revolutionary theory of alcoholism causation and treatment, has received excellent reviews at workshops and conferences including university, professional, and public settings. These theories were also warmly received when presented at a national conference in Baltimore, Maryland, in 1982 and a statewide conference of counselors in Columbus, Ohio, in 1984. Presently, I am a private practitioner and consultant in addition to giving lectures and workshops on alcoholism and recovery.

Never before has such a broad experience and wealth of knowledge about alcoholism been assimilated by one person. I have accomplished this and now share it within this book for the sole purpose of helping alcoholics and their families recover. Moreover, it is done with a common sense approach and writing style that assures understandability by the average person. In addition, even the most seasoned counselor of alcoholics will benefit from this information. In fact, it is predicted that this book will be a handbook for clinicians and a "bible" for recovering alcoholics and their families everywhere.

A brief explanation of how this book came to be written might be helpful in understanding its purpose. When my drinking stopped in 1974, an immediate objective was to repair the wreckage caused by twenty-three years of active alcoholism. It was decided that the best way to accomplish my task and remain sober was to help others who also suffer from this terrible disease. Therefore, my motivation toward helping others is tinged with a bit of selfishness. Most assuredly, help was needed, but it was also reasoned that helping others get sober would help me stay that way. Moreover, it was obvious that most people, including myself, did not understand the disease of alcoholism or how it should be treated.

Consequently, my first objective was to learn about alcoholism. I knew how to get drunk and understood the problem from that point of view, but didn't know how to get sober or what it meant. More importantly, those who were trying to rehabilitate alcoholics didn't know how to help us get sober either. They knew something, but it wasn't nearly enough. I needed to learn what they knew and couple that with the information gained from twenty three-years of drinking. In that way, it was reasoned, my knowledge base would be complete. It would then be possible to tell them, the counselors, how to help us, the alcoholics.

In the process of acquiring the necessary knowledge, I earned four college degrees—a Bachelor's degree in Social Psychology, a Masters in Mental Health Counseling, a Masters in Rehabilitation Counseling, and a Ph.D. in Counseling Psychology. As an incentive, to those of you who might doubt your ability to rehabilitate, this was all done in six years time. In my estimation, anyone can accomplish a similar recovery if properly informed and motivated. The information on how to do it is contained within this book, but only the alcoholic knows the seriousness of his intentions.

More important than the college degrees, of course, was the knowledge gained therefrom. It's rather difficult to say when the "missing link" was found between what was known to me already and what was found within the books. That information might have been acquired at any one of the educational levels but it didn't dawn on me until the doctoral level of study. When, where, and how it happened is unimportant. The important thing is that the message began to take shape. I knew what had to be conveyed not only to the counselor who is trying to help us, but also to everyone suffering from alcoholism.

Prior to making this information available to the public, however, my theories had to be tested in actual practice. This was accomplished over a seven year period of time in which both inpatient and outpatient settings were utilized. The settings were carefully selected ones which provided treatment to both the alcoholic and the entire family. During these years of clinical application, my theories were adjusted. Old or invalid concepts were replaced with new and valid ones. This process resulted in the "polished" product presented within this book. Although the process of polishing one's theories and approaches to counseling is never complete (we learn from every session), the theories reach an optimum level of worth. My knowledge, experience and theories about how to help those suffering from alcoholism has reached such a level of worth and are ready to be shared with the public.

I have no doubt that all alcoholics and significant others have within themselves the potential for recovery. This book can provide one with the ability to find and release that potential. A word of caution, however. This is a self-help book with limitations. The information contained herein will only help the reader reach a decision relative to his or her needs. Corrective action can be most difficult requiring professional help. Therefore, please seek the aid of a qualified alcoholism rehabilitation counselor, most generally listed in the yellow pages under "Alcoholism Treatment".

About Alcoholism: A Common Sense Perspective is written purposefully in a plain and common sense language that could only be done by one who has been there and back. As indicated, it is based on my lifetime experience with alcoholism which includes all possible aspects of the problem. These experiences were collectively concentrated in addressing myself to the task of writing this book which was years in the making. These years were not all spent writing, of course, but mostly in formulating thoughts and theories in such a way that insures maximum reader understanding.

In my estimation, the extent of one's knowledge of a subject has a direct relationship with his ability to simplify and break this knowledge down into a common sense perspective. Simply stated, this means that knowledge gained from reading a common sense perspective book can be applied to the task of everyday living. In order to effectively provide the reader such a service, the writer must have a full and complete comprehension of his subject matter. To gain such comprehension of alcoholism and recovery, one's background should include at least certain minimal qualifications. He, for example, must have suffered the depths of alcoholism and be recovering from it. In addition, he must have not only studied the subject thoroughly but, hopefully, also taught it. Finally, he must have been both patient and doctor of alcoholism. These experiences and more compile my background on this subject and are shared with you herein as simply as possible.

Any approach to the problem of helping others understand the complicated disease of alcoholism must be especially plain and simple. How, for example, can we expect an alcoholic, whose mind is affected by the disease, to unravel complex theorems and understand complicated terms? For that matter, how can we expect the family members to do so when their minds are confused with the frustration of it all and, they, themselves, are denying reality. This will be discussed in detail within chapter four.

It is high time we quit trying to explain away every problem of the human organism by statistical analyses and empirical studies. On the contrary, we need to take a hard, common sense approach to life and its problems. We gain knowledge from our readings and wisdom from our experience and if we combine and assimilate the two, we have common sense.

All of you now reading this introduction are either experiencing a problem with alcoholism, have done so, or more than likely will. Being an alcoholic, the son of one, and caught in the web of alcoholism all my life, I can relate to you. This will be seen more clearly after reading the prologue entitled "A Profile of An Alcoholic", in which the reader is exposed to a pitiful and horrible picture of alcoholism as only one who has experienced it can describe. For clarification purposes, personal aspects of my alcoholic background are shared in vivid detail. Included are experiences in the military, jails, mental institutions and my home life. In addition, horrors of mental institution confinement and mistreatment resulting from incorrect or incomplete diagnoses are highlighted. The reader cannot help but feel some of the pain as the sad experience of my insane drinking history is shared.

Along with sadness, however, the reader emerges with hope, because my own recovery process shows the possibility of regaining sanity where it was lost, respect where there was none, and life where suicide was imminent. It is reasoned that if one alcoholic family can turn this nightmarish experience around, then it is possible for others to do likewise. Through understanding the concepts contained herein, I sincerely believe all can recover from alcoholism whether one is alcoholic or a significant other.

It is important that the prologue be read carefully because it is a "springboard" for that which follows. Although it might seem that my experiences are unique, they are typical of alcoholism and shared for that purpose. Many aspects of the disease, for example, are contained within the prologue and referred to in later chapters. The reader is cautioned not to be misled by my simplistic writing style. Very important concepts of alcoholism could be missed by only "glossing" over this section of the book.

The remainder of the book is developed in much the same plain, common sense writing style as the prologue. For those who enjoy technical writing, however, please refer to my Doctoral Thesis entitled, *The Effects of Anxiety Awareness on Campus Drinking Behavior: A Possible Etiological Factor* (University of Toledo 1981). My original and revolutionary theories of alcoholism causation and treatment are contained within my Doctoral work. These theories, although complex, are explained in a plain, common sense language within chapters two and three respectively of this book.

Also, information shared with the reader continues to be based on a global background in alcoholism. The reader, for example, is guaranteed a better working knowledge of this terrible disease after reading chapter one, "Understanding Alcoholism". By working knowledge, I mean information that can be applied to daily situations relative to the disease. It also means that the reader's time will not be wasted with statistical data and research findings not relative to a common sense perspective.

Within chapter two, entitled "Alcoholism Causation", several causative theories will be discussed. My theory of causation will be highlighted within that chapter and should prove to be very interesting. Since it is difficult to speak very long on the subject of causation without getting technical, chapter two will be brief in keeping with my promise that the reader will not be confused or bored by technical jargon. Unfortunately, the reader might be disappointed if he expects to find a conclusive answer to the cause of alcoholism. There is none. We neither know what causes it, nor offer a cure for alcoholism as of this writing.

Regardless of your relationship with the disease of alcoholism, chapter three will be extremely helpful. Within that chapter, the treatment component of my theory is explained in detail. This will provide the reader with an opportunity to gain a solid foundation of how the transition from futility to respectability is made. Moreover, the awareness of this process will help both the alcoholic and significant other. They will gain, for example, a better appreciation for the destructive nature of the disease.

More importantly, all involved with the alcoholic's plight, not only the alcoholic, but also significant others, will be encouraged that recovery is possible. In addition, professional counselors should appreciate the detailed explanation of my treatment theory presented in conjunction with a step by step explanation of application procedures. Finally, it is discussed within chapter three why most present day treatment approaches, although far superior to yesterday's, are still falling short of intended goals.

Within chapter four, treatment issues relative to the family and significant others are addressed specifically. As stated in the beginning of this introduction, the non-drinking person associated with alcoholism is often times in dire need of treatment. Once again, in a very clear and understandable language, new and workable concepts relative to family treatment are presented. Finally, "adult child of alcoholic" issues are discussed.

The text is concluded with chapter five in which are discussed two very important self-help groups available to us. These are Alcoholics Anonymous (AA) and Alanon. AA, of course, is the most effective single component of recovery available to the alcoholic. Alanon provides similar support for significant others, especially the spouse and family. Also within this final chapter, I discuss issues of AA with explanations of the "Twelve Steps" that will prove invaluable to not only the new AA member, but also the long-time recovering alcoholic. Both the alcoholic and significant other will benefit from answers to such questions as "What are AA and Alanon and what can they do for me?" and "What is expected of me if I do join?" These questions are answered with a vivid recollection of my first AA meeting. Even though twenty years has elapsed since then, those early difficulties in accepting AA are still fresh in my mind. Information contained within chapter five will help others make a better initial adjustment into either an AA or Alanon program.

Finally, chapter five concludes with a discussion about halfway houses and the more expensive acute care facility. It is brought out that a middle ground must be established between the two. For example, insurance companies and the general public can not continue paying more than twenty times the cost of halfway house treatment for the more elaborate hospital settings. This is especially true when recidivism rates are so high in alcoholism rehabilitation.

Terminology understanding is assured by the glossary of words presented following a short epilogue. There is also a handy cross reference within the glossary whereby complex terminology is replaced with a more common sense and understandable language.

Finally, many illustrations, charts and other graphic materials are used throughout to clarify, support, and further explain the concepts presented herein. It is my hope that this book will accomplish the task for which it is intended. Very simply stated, this book is meant to help the alcoholic and his significant others gain stability in their lives. Relax and enjoy this book for there are no statistical studies or ponderous quotes to confuse or bore you. Seventy-five cent words are at an absolute minimum (but used occasionally as I succumb to the temptation of flaunting my Ph.D. just a little).

ACKNOWLEDGEMENTS

Kathryn Rosumny Anderson, who provided the necessary inspiration at the beginning of this book and support throughout its writing. Kathy also had the thankless task of proof reading for an author who does not accept criticism graciously. It is no small accomplishment that Kathy and I are still the best of friends. This, in spite of her much appreciated criticism.

Karen Dixon: My girl Friday. Without Karen's assistance, this book might not have reached completion for another year. She did all of the typing, retyping and retyping of the manuscript. She interpreted my hen scratches and somehow got them into the computer legibly. Karen kicked me in to production when I got lazy and insisted that I relax when overextended. All and all, I owe an unmeasurable gratitude to Karen that would be most difficult to repay. Fortunately for me, all Karen wants in return is friendship. This she will always have.

William E. Staccia, my older brother.

James R. Staccia, my younger brother.

Ms. Valerie C. Hack, close friend and confidante.

A special thanks to all my relatives, friends, neighbors and lodge brothers, all of whom have been very supportive.

Cover designed by Katharina E. Warner.

About Alcoholism: A Common Sense Perspective

PROLOGUE

(PROFILE OF AN ALCOHOLIC):

In March of 1974, I awoke sprawled across a bed in the Springfield, Ohio, mental health facility with the sun shining in my eyes. My mind was blank except for a vague memory of the night before. It seemed that I was at a friend's house. He and someone else were arguing with me. They were saying I needed help and trying to convince me to go somewhere. That was eight o'clock at night. Obviously, there had been another blackout (see glossary). Although scary, that was nothing new because blackouts had become more frequent and severe as my alcoholism progressed. In fact, that morning in 1974 culminated twenty-three years of drinking.

I was thirty-seven years old, jobless, broke, had a bad conduct discharge after twelve years in the military, was divorced and had only an eighth grade education. My drinking was alcoholic almost from the start and directly responsible for my having been in jail in four different countries and six different states. It was also drinking that caused me to have been confined in five different mental institutions. Finally, alcoholism had caused my family, friends, and even myself to be ashamed of such a drunken bum. They avoided me; I couldn't.

It wasn't always that way, however. In fact, I was born in a "dry" county of Kentucky in a log house on Indian Creek just outside of West Liberty. My biological father was an alcoholic and deserted

1

my mother, older brother and me when I was an infant. My mother moved us to Springfield, Ohio, a year later.

Growing up in Springfield was difficult. We lived in the poorest section of town which was no problem. Life outside that section, however, was a daily trauma. My elementary school was located in the "rich" part of town, some thirteen blocks from home. Most of those blocks were outside of my element and walking them was difficult. We all know how kids can be extremely cruel to other kids, especially if there is a difference in color, dress, actions, etc. These kids were no different. They would laugh and make fun of my hand-me-down clothing and hillbilly accent.

Then one day a bully mistakenly confused my shy, withdrawn acceptance of verbal abuse for that of being a coward. With his friends' encouragement, he finally hit me. Even though he was older and bigger, there was no match. Unleashed on that poor kid were years of pent up anger and hurt. When his buddies were invited to partake, they declined and as word of this fight spread, the laughter and ridicule diminished. I was nine years old at the time and learned a very important street-rule: might makes right. I never projected a weak image again, but remained my own worst critic. Although I now see escape into alcohol as a weakness, the intended image was strength. In fact, I saw drinking and its associated behavior as being manly which, of course, represents strength to a kid.

My first drink of alcohol was taken four years later at the age of thirteen. It was a pleasant experience, in which my natural shyness and feelings of inferiority were immediately forgotten and replaced by a feeling of equality with the world. My drinking continued gradually through the eighth grade of school and contributed to my quitting school a year later without having completed the first month of the ninth grade.

At that time, being sixteen years old, I went to work in a factory. My bring home pay was $37.50 per week of which $25.00 was turned over to help with home expenses. The rest was spent on drinking and having "fun". In 1953, $12.50 was easily enough to get drunk Friday and Saturday nights, sober up Sunday and return to work Monday morning. I joined the Armed Forces on my seventeenth birthday and eventually had twelve years of active duty. My alcoholism progression went into high gear while I was in the military, but that was not necessarily their fault. Such is the nature of the disease. Marrying the girl I dated from age fifteen, I had a wife and son to support when honorably discharged in 1958.

Since this country was experiencing a post Korean War depression in 1958, jobs were scarce. Construction work being the only thing available, I took it until winter closed even that down two months later. Once again, I was unemployed. Twenty dollars a week unemployment compensation just wasn't enough to support my family and my drinking. Therefore, the family decision was that I should reenter the military.

Increasing at a steady rate while in the service, my drinking contributed to an overall dissatisfaction with the military. A decision to get out at the end of my enlistment in 1963 was changed by the Kennedy assassination. All essential personnel were "frozen" for an additional year. At that time, it was decided to reenlist for another four years and collect the bonus. My alcoholism was fully manifested by this time and this proved to be my last enlistment.

Drinking finally reached a state of causing dramatic complications for me in 1965. It happened while on duty in Southeast Asia. One Wednesday morning I woke up in a village fifty kilometers from base. The last thing I remembered was drinking in a club on base Sunday night. I had been absent without official leave (AWOL) since Monday. To make a long story short, my absence lasted six months. As a result of breaking this military law, I received a Special Courts Martial which resulted in a Bad Conduct Discharge, six months in the stockade at hard labor, being reduced to the lowest rank, and forfeiture of two-thirds pay. My military career was over.

Reentry into civilian life was traumatic as the conquering hero returned in shame. My family had grown to four children and my drinking was now continuous. Job after job was lost because of my alcoholism, but in 1966, jobs were easy to find because Vietnam was really hot. The drinking began causing me other complications. My mind and body began reacting to the beating imposed upon it. I started having nervous anxiety (see glossary) which, to a certain extent, was a carry-over from the military. I did not feel close to anyone. It was hard to relate to a long haired hippie who wanted to talk about how "*mean his machine was*" and how easy it was to "*dodge the draft*". I was very lonely with nothing but a bottle and old memories to keep me company. I was also scared; scared of everything that moved or made a sound. I slept with a loaded gun within easy reach and, while in a bar, always sat with my back against the wall. The alcohol was contributing to my irrational fears which were getting progressively worse, but I didn't know it.

In 1967, I was persuaded to see a psychiatrist. Psychiatrists, however, are medical doctors with specific training in the fields of organic brain diseases and mental illness. Alcoholism is a primary disease of unknown origin. It is neither a mental illness in the classic sense nor an organic brain disease. Because of their training, however, psychiatrists invariably see alcoholism as a secondary symptom of some underlying mental problem. My condition, for example, was not diagnosed as alcoholism, but acute anxiety reaction. Conversely, an alcoholism rehabilitation counselor would have seen the problem differently and made an assessment of alcoholism. As will be shown, my experience with psychiatrists traumatically complicated my recovery. This is true because they treated for the diagnosed anxiety reaction and not alcoholism. In reflection, the diagnosis of alcoholism was never made in all my experience with the psychiatric profession. This is almost unbelievable.

The psychiatrist continued treating me for anxiety reaction. He made a connection between my many years of military service, extended overseas duty in Southeast Asia, Appalachian background, job, and other factors contributing to my anxiety reaction. Upon release from the psychiatric hospital, I was advised, once again, to slow down, relax, and quit drinking so much. Once again, I didn't drink so much, but drank more. Within less than three months, it was back to the hospital where I was dried out again and released. A month later, I awoke there again. This time, my roommate was an admitted alcoholic experiencing difficulty withdrawing from alcohol.

His behavior seemed bizarre and unpredictable, so I talked about myself in an effort to quiet him. As my story was related highlighting the difficulties of nervous anxiety, he seemed interested and calmed down considerably. I continued telling him all about my terrible experiences in jails and mental institutions. Inadvertently, I must have included my drinking history because he made one of the most meaningful and profound statements affecting my life to that time and, possibly forever. He said, "Buddy, I don't know you from Adam, but I will tell you what your problem is. You can forget about anxiety reaction and extended Southeast Asian duty complications. That's all nothing but bull. You, my friend, are an alcoholic." At that time, I had been in three different psychiatric hospitals, including two in the military, and that term had never been directed toward me or used in any capacity relative to my condition.

As a result of that conversation, the realization dawned on me that my problem might be alcohol. At that time, I was thirty-one years old and had drank for eighteen years. I had been jailed several times as a result of alcohol, kicked out of the military because of alcohol, hospitalized in psychiatric wards because of alcohol and lost job after job as a result of alcohol. That was in 1967, and it wasn't yet through with me.

The next morning, I talked with my doctor, a psychiatrist, and asked him if I might be an alcoholic. He said that was a possibility and agreed to treat me as such. He prescribed Antabuse (Disulfiram), a chemical in pill form which, when taken daily, mixes adversely with alcohol. For my nerves, he prescribed Miltown tranquilizers in the pill form, each containing 400 milligrams. My experience with this latter "medication" was traumatic.

At first, the tranquilizers calmed my nerves immediately and relieved all of my symptoms; the effect was miraculous. My fears and anxiety were gone and nothing upset me. The wife and family could be tolerated. Working in the confined quarters of a factory became less frightening. Gone was the fear of going crazy while watching that machine go back and forth. No longer were the walls closing in on me and work in a factory actually began to seem attractive. The drinking had stopped and my medication was working. The pills were taken as prescribed: one-half Antabuse daily and Miltown every four hours at 8 AM, 12 PM, 4 PM, and at 8 PM, *or as needed.* These last three words were my undoing.

After about two or three weeks, I noticed an overwhelming nervousness at about 11 AM. My prescription did say "as needed" so I started taking my pill at 8 AM, 11 AM, 2 PM, 5 PM, and at 8 PM. It worked, yet in less than two weeks, I became nervous at around 10 AM. No problem. I took the pill at 8, 10, 12, 2, 4, 6, 8 and, because I was having trouble going to sleep, at 10 PM. Within a week, the nervousness was almost overwhelming by 9 AM so I began taking Miltown every hour.

My work efficiency fell off and was not satisfactory overall because of an inability to follow blueprint specifications. It required an alert mind to do the intricate and precise machining necessary and I was scrapping piece after very expensive piece. The foreman recommended sick leave which was gladly accepted. Work no longer held the feeling of accomplishment that it had during the beginning of my pill taking. No longer did work seem attractive because for some reason, I just could not perform well. Of course, my system was developing an addiction to Miltown tranquilizer.

Instead of the factory, bars once again became a regular hangout. My daily routine consisted of sitting on a bar stool all day, drinking Pepsi and popping pills. In retrospect, it is almost comical to reflect on how ignorant I was about the addiction process. This can be seen by an example of my conversation with other bar patrons to whom I would explain to them about having a "former" problem with alcohol and how great it was to be cured. Of course, I was probably more intoxicated (on pills) than anyone in the bar. Today, it is almost unbelievable that I could have been so stupid. Any fool should be able to recognize that one addiction (pills) was being substituted for another (alcohol). That was almost twenty years ago and similar foolishness, unfortunately, is being practiced today. As the song says, "When will they ever learn?"

As the pills were eaten with increased frequency, my mental and physical stability deteriorated. It became impossible for me to walk straight enough to make it to a bar anymore. Thank God a car was not available as my condition continued to worsen. My existence at home consisted of downing pills, watching television and passing out in a drugged stupor. Finally, my wife gave the doctor an ultimatum: either he do something to stop this steady progression to death or she would no longer be responsible. The doctor, who was writing my prescriptions, finally heard her. She was told to bring me to the hospital. In less than six months, I had gone from taking one pill every four hours, or as needed, to consuming more than 8,000 milligrams of Miltown per day.

One might wonder why the doctor continued writing prescriptions at such an increasing frequency. Well, I lied to him. It must be stated, however, that he was not difficult to deceive. Excuses such as, *I lost my pills*, or *Someone broke into my car and stole my pills*, were readily accepted without question. But the excuse used time and again was, "Angie, my youngest daughter, flushed them down the toilet drain." That excuse was used so many times that, if true, every fish in the local river would have been high enough to walk on water.

My experience with prescribed addiction highlights the dangers of treating alcohol and drug addiction with drugs. I never bought a pill illegally, unless we accept my lying as illegal. Yet, my daily intake of more than 20 pills, each containing 400 milligrams, exceeded five times the prescribed dosage. It is sad to say that, although this happened to me almost twenty years ago, prescription addiction is even more prevalent today. The alcoholic will almost always develop a similar type of reaction to such mood altering (see glossary) "medication" as thus described. Helping victims of this complicated addiction to rehabilitate comprises much of my daily practice. While it was easy for me to reach my level of addiction, it was much more difficult to recover.

When my wife admitted me to the psychiatric ward in a coma-tose-like state, the doctor felt that further medication might be dangerous or ineffective because my system was so saturated. As a result of that decision, I withdrew from more than 8,000 milligrams of Miltown tranquilizer per day Cold Turkey (See Glossary). That was an experience. There were no severe problems the first forty-eight hours, but then I began experiencing dramatic and exaggerated mood swings. The feeling of happiness, for example, would change to one of sadness or deep depression unexpectedly.

Eventually, an overall emotion of fear encompassed me. It was a fear of everyone and every noise. It was a fear of going crazy and of dying. The walls seemed to be closing in and panic reactions would ebb and flow. I wanted to run, but couldn't. I wanted to be left alone, but wasn't. The fear of dying was a constant one as my heart rate increased dramatically and my temples pounded. My fear was projected onto the other patients. It was visible in their eyes as my confused mind tried to re-establish sanity within itself. Suspicions and mistrusts were absolutely overwhelming. Everyone, especially the staff, was perceived as scheming and plotting against me.

As the dilemma continued, my confused mind flashed back to experiences in Southeast Asia and mixed them with more recent experiences. The hallucinations seemed so real and were so intense that many of them are still vivid within my mind today. One in particular has such an outstanding clarity that I still joke with my older brother about it. It seems that he was on a bulldozer outside the psychiatric unit with intentions of rescuing me. He was yelling to me and I to him as we attempted to determine the weakest part of the building's structure. He was going to knock down the wall with the dozer and get me out of that place. The other patients withdrew fearfully and watched as I talked with my imaginary rescuer. My delusions continued with both verbal and visual hallucinations. Some of the voices were threatening as various perceived enemies from my past were conjured up. Some were pacifying, such as my mother telling me everything would be okay, just hold on.

The intensity of my experience had peaks and valleys. It seemed to be over at one time and reality replaced delusion, but then it started over again. I now know why, but at the time, I didn't. The reason is that hard drugs such as pills leave the system differently than alcohol. Each drug, for example, has a different half-life (see glossary) and therefore, is expelled from the body at a less predictable rate than does alcohol. Stored within the cells of the body, hard drugs take longer to leave and do so within a cyclic time frame, depending on their half-life. In other words, one might be perfectly normal for a while, but then the chemical being stored in the tissue is released. When this happens, one gets high all over again.

The staff was incapable of helping to diminish my fears of going crazy. They unknowingly contributed with such statements as, "Well, you had a bad day, but the drug should be out of your system now. I don't know why you are still having these episodes." My conclusion, based on an 8th grade education and a perception of the staff as being knowledgeable, was simple. I must be crazy if the drug was not causing my behavior.

Finally, on the fourth or fifth day and night of this living nightmare, another peak in the intensity of my withdrawal process was reached. I went berzerk and tried to escape by breaking through the door of the psych unit. Police were summoned to assist the orderlies and together they subdued me by strapping me down. The head nurse then gave me an injection that put me out until the following morning. I was then confronted by the psychiatrist who informed me that the local hospital could not contain me any longer and that he would be transferring me to a state mental institution.

This was in 1967-68 and alcohol rehabilitation units of today were not available to the average working man. Thank God that has changed. Excellent treatment is available, at least for detoxification (see glossary), for virtually everyone. Unfortunately, little has changed in the psychiatric approach to the problem of alcoholism or drug addiction. In fairness to the psychiatric profession, however, it is necessary to mention certain aspects of this problem. First, the psychiatrist, in general, perceives alcoholism as a symptom or sign of some underlying disturbance within the individual. In my own experience, the psychiatrist treated me for anxiety, reactive type. Simply stated, this means that I reacted to certain stressful situations by manifesting anxiety. This provided an excuse to avoid the stressful situation. Consequently, each time the situation presented itself, I had a built in avoidance mechanism. Therefore, dealing with the anxiety producing issue at the conscious level was unnecessary.

According to theory, one rarely knows what the real problem is at the conscious level, but carries this knowledge at the subconscious level of thought. He will consciously identify a relatively harmless object as the problem, which is somehow connected with the real issue. My job, for example, was identified as a problem. It was a problem--a daily one. I absolutely hated working in that factory and after twelve years of military life, factory work readjustment was just impossible. The psychiatrist continually discouraged quitting the job, however, and, I suspect, felt that something within the factory was an underlying cause for my anxiety. The machine itself, for example, might have posed some threat to my subconscious. My real problem might have been a co-worker who was either a direct threat or a threat through subconscious association with a past enemy. Of course, my psychiatrist never shared with me any of his theories. One can only guess as to what he suspected was my real problem.

My factory experience is shared with the reader to illustrate why the classic psychiatric approach has limited treatment success with alcoholics. This is simply because its approach to treating the alcoholic was to use a mood altering medication (tranquilizers). The psychiatrist and medical profession, in general, have experienced difficulty in even minimal rehabilitation success of the alcoholic for this reason. The alcoholic will invariably become addicted to the medication as I did. When viewed from the perspective of the medical profession, which includes psychiatrists, this is understandable because it is based on a treatment by medication. Unfortunately, there is no pill that will cure alcoholism. Russian scientists claimed to have developed such a pill two or three years ago. It did seem to effectively reduce one's alcohol intake, but caused a severe addiction to the pill. Does that sound familiar? As stated earlier, using a drug to treat any type of chemical addiction is like pouring water on a drowning person.

My experience with the conversion from alcohol to Miltown is typical. Similar mistreatment of the alcoholic by those not schooled in the addiction process is seen almost daily within my practice. The client will invariably relate how the family physician advised something for nerves. Usually, a drinking history was shared with the physician in which even the novice counselor would assess alcoholism. On the other hand, if the alcoholic is not properly diagnosed and is prescribed Valium, Librium, Ativan, Mellaril or, heaven forbid, Thorazine, more problems are conceivable.

Prescription addiction is easy to assess. Typically, the client is sitting in my office with eyes as big as saucers, licking his lips and making about as much sense as a babbling idiot. He invariably relates that he no longer drinks, but still can't perform at work, in sexual relationships, or just in every day life. In answer to the question of medication intake, they usually present a handful of pills that some general practitioner prescribed. I usually usher them to the restroom where the "junk" is flushed down the drain. If necessary, the client is then sent to a treatment center that does not use such an approach in treating the alcoholic.

There is a certain population for which the psychiatrist is needed because alcohol is camouflaging real mental problems. In these cases, once the alcohol (a sedative) is removed, bizarre behavior will ensue. In other words, alcohol was keeping the individual sufficiently sedated to render him harmless. This person requires medical treatment from a psychiatrist usually with what is referred to as psychotropic drugs such as those previously mentioned. In fact, my experience in mental wards, both as a patient and clinician, convinces me that there are many patients who are potentially dangerous to self and/or others and are in dire need of psychiatric care. It is imperative that the alcoholism counselor be qualified to recognize this and refer accordingly. Psychiatrists likewise might consider referring their alcoholics to alcoholism counselors, if necessary.

That did not happen to me, however, and through the psychiatrist's recommendation, I was court ordered to the state mental institution in early 1968. It was a terrible experience. For the first thirty days of evaluation and processing, everyone was housed together in a large, one hundred bed dormitory. Hard core drug addicts and alcoholics were put in with all types of mentally ill patients. Persons suspected or convicted of various aberrant criminal activity were also in the "holding tank". Rapists, homosexuals, child molestors, murderers, arsonists and habitual criminals with varied leanings were all mixed within the same population. Thorazine was the equalizor. Of course, there were those with mental and emotional problems ranging from mild to very severe. We all seemed to gravitate toward one of three sub-groups consisting of: 1) alcoholics and drug addicts; 2) criminals; or 3) crazies. It may sound cruel to make such a statement but, unfortunately, it is true. I went in as a crazy.

You might recall that my diagnosis was not alcoholism. It started as simple anxiety reaction but was later changed to schizophrenia, paranoid type. This latter diagnosis is reserved for those with very serious mental impairment, including delusions and hallucinations with an inability to perceive reality. In other words, we usually visualize one with this condition as acting like Napoleon and seeing those around him as soldiers. This person might be dangerous if everyone is seen as the enemy. Otherwise, he is just difficult to interact with, unless one is used to taking orders.

Seriously, my diagnosis established a treatment approach relegated to one with a very serious mental impairment. Not that this

implies one sickness is better than the other, but it is like treating
for a broken leg when one has athlete's foot. Of course, this stuff
was all Greek back then and it just about freaked me out when my
diagnosis was changed to schizophrenia undifferentiated. Now I
know that meant they just didn't know what to make of me. This
might have been the first step in the right direction on my behalf.

How did all this happen? There was nothing within my medical
history suggesting such an extensive and serious mental disorder—
that is, not until the drug-induced episode caused by Miltown withdrawal described earlier. There was, of course, alcohol related, stupid, unpredictable behavior, but that is the nature of alcoholism.
Why was I given Miltown tranquilizor? That was to calm my nerves
when the alcohol was removed, remember? Obviously, my addiction
to alcohol was replaced with an addiction to hard drugs.

There were at least two good things that happened to me while at
the state mental institution (excuse me if I can't call it a hospital).
First of all, I came to realize by process of elimination that I wasn't
crazy. The second thing was that I came to admit my alcoholism.
This was not due to therapy, but because of the one Alcoholics
Anonymous (AA) meeting I attended while a patient there. Although AA will be explained in detail within chapter five, a brief
mention of its procedure will be made here. In the classic lead meeting, a guest speaker relates his life story relative to alcoholism. After
listening to the lead that night, I had no doubt of my alcoholism.
His story so closely paralleled mine that if the speaker were alcoholic, surely I was.

My emotions were mixed. Alcoholism might explain some of my
past crazy behavior, therefore, I wasn't crazy. On the other hand, I
didn't want to be an alcoholic either. This required a great deal of
thought. Upon discharge, I went straight across the street to a bar
and ordered a double double shot of whiskey after telling the bar-
tender that I was alcoholic. That was in March of 1968.

Yes, I was an admitted alcoholic and for six more years, admitted
it to everyone, especially if they would buy me a drink. My drinking
continued to worsen. Just to buy a drink, I would steal from my
wife's purse the money she needed to buy groceries and pay bills.
Life for me became one big con game in order to buy drink. When I
couldn't buy it or con for it, I stole it. When times would get really
difficult, I would work a while. During these periods, I would kid
myself and family that my drinking days were over. These terms of
sobriety were short, however, usually lasting just long enough for
me to catch up on the bills and regain the good graces of my family

and friends. Also during these times, a month or so at most, my drinking would be more controlled and confined to home. My wife would become more tolerant and forgiving and gradually the *heat* would dissipate. Then, after a while, it would be the same old thing. My old pattern of getting really drunk, not coming home for two or three nights, losing my job, and being on the bum would repeat itself.

I tried going to Florida to find a job even though there were plenty of jobs in Ohio. This provided me an excuse to escape from the people who were getting tired of my behavior. Next, I got a job in San Diego, California, but lost it when put in the Tijuana, Mexico, jail because of foolish drunken behavior. I went to Denver, Colorado, worked for Manpower and managed to stay drunk there for a while.

When the going got really tough, I went back home to "start a new life" without alcohol. My self-defeat convinced me of my sincerity, but others were getting tired of my lies. It sounded convincing though, because my wife wanted to believe me. Once again, construction work was available to me. I fell off the roof of a house one day and was fired. Because of being drunk, no bones were broken when I landed in soft excavated dirt around the foundation of the house. The accident gave me a welcomed opportunity to stay home and drink in peace without guilt.

As my alcoholism progressed, my control of alcohol was lost and it seemed impossible to stop. I actually cursed the bottle prior to taking a drink. Suicide was often a very strong thought, especially when no one was available from whom to con, beg, borrow or steal a drink. When all else failed, there was Mom. I can still see the sad look in her eyes as she watched me walk onto the porch. Recognizing my pain, she would go to the back room and return with a couple of dollars and say, "Here, go get something to get well on. You are in bad shape." I felt like a bum and was, but still took her money.

My nerves would be so bad that going into a bar was impossible. It was impossible to sit still long enough to get the drink down. It seemed like everyone was watching me. I would go to a carry-out, one that was not crowded, and get a pint of wine. Usually, this would quiet the shakes and calm my fears sufficiently to enable me to get drunk again in a bar. My nerves would be calm enough to win a game of pool for drinking money or pick up a female who had money. The next day, it would start over again. Finally, my wife threw in the towel!

We were at the house of a friend, a fellow veteran, who previously had volunteered to transport me to the Chillicothe, Ohio, V.A. Hospital for alcoholism treatment. But I tricked him! My friend made the mistake of giving me a twenty dollar bill when he dropped me off at the hospital. I never checked myself into the hospital, but instead hitched a ride back to Springfield where the drinking insanity continued.

Once again, my friend offered help. He called my wife who emphatically stated she was done with me, but as a last favor, wanted to get me help. In short, it was either go to the hospital or get out into the cold. Confronted by such determination, I agreed to really go this time, "just as soon as I finished my bottle". It was about six PM and the bottle was over half full. My wife agreed and shortly thereafter, I recall talking about the military with my friend. The next thing I knew, the morning sun was in my face and it was eight AM. My first thoughts were that it was a V.A. hospital, but discovered it was the mental health clinic.

Mental health clinics were just getting started in 1974. They were built to provide a service to the mentally ill and emotionally disturbed clients while housing them within their own community. Treatment consisted of inpatient care, followed by a structured *day care* or outpatient program. The client then reported to the mental health facility on a daily basis while living at home. The mental health movement helped to lessen the possibility of alcoholics being placed in mental institutions resulting from misdiagnosis. Inaccurate diagnoses did occur and, unfortunately will continue, but the consequences at present are not nearly so traumatic. Ohio still does not have chemically dependent specialists within these facilities to control the treatment of alcoholics and drug addicts. More progressive states do, however, and are seeing excellent results. Fortunately for me, there was little doubt as to my needs when I awoke that morning in March, 1974.

I was placed in the alcoholism component of the care facility. The entire program consisted of three meetings a week and was supervised by two people, a registered nurse and a recovering alcoholic with no counselor training. We met for group discussion Monday, education Wednesday, and group discussion again on Friday. Each session consisted of two hours. The remainder of time was spent in general population activities. Admittedly, the clinic was lacking when compared to today's treatment facilities, but a giant step forward from 1968.

The group discussions did very little in the way of motivating me or solidifying the acceptance of my disease of alcoholism. The educational component, however, was exceptional for that time. I can still visualize the movie portraying a Canadian physician talking about alcohol and its destructive impact on the human mind and body. I swear to this day that no one ever told me such facts about alcoholism before. The realization that my body had brain damage, liver damage and nerve tissue damage among other things caused me to stare in disbelief.

I became more active during the group discussions in order to learn more. I asked Tom, the recovering alcoholic, and Marge, the nurse, if they agreed that alcohol destroyed the mind and body like it was stated in the film. Both did. Surprisingly, the other group members were also in agreement. At that time, I realized and truly accepted not only my alcoholism, but also its destructive nature. Furthermore, a vow was made against drinking if my mind and body were able to recover from the damage. My recovery started in earnest from that date.

Of course, recovery in the past was a game with me. I would attend AA meetings periodically since being released from the mental institution in 1968. The interaction with other alcoholics provided me a false sense of "doing something about my alcoholism". It also helped convince others that I really meant business. All in all, I must have quit drinking a hundred times before. This time, however, there was something different about my feelings and thoughts. During previous efforts, I wanted others to compliment me and give me credit for "doing a good job". Also, I wanted instant recovery which meant a good job, respectability and acceptance as an upright citizen. When it didn't come, I would get drunk on the premise that there was no use. Nobody would give me a break. That method worked most effectively on persons closest to me, such as my wife, parents, and relatives. But this time, in 1974, the thoughts and opinions of others meant very little.

Not only did the opinions of others not affect me this time, but also they were not part of my thoughts. In other words, I didn't say to myself or others that it didn't matter what so-and-so said about me; I just didn't address the issue. The best barometer for gauging the sincerity of the recovering alcoholic might just be whether or not they seek approval from others. In my particular case, the opinions of others meant very little once I really meant business.

The same old gossip relative to my *quitting again* went something like this: "I'll give him a week and he'll be drunk again; give him a month; he will never last six months; maybe he means business this time." But after the first year, folks were saying, "He really means it." Today, I am no longer seen as the family drunkard and people who recognize me walking down the street do not cross in order to avoid contact. It's great that people do respect me now and actually seek my companionship. It really doesn't make any difference what "they" say or think, however, because their opinions are not important to my sobriety effort.

My first effort toward real recovery was to set goals and methods by which to accomplish them. My primary goal was to be a real counselor of alcoholics. The experience in mental hospitals and the so-called recovery programs taught me that the field of alcoholism rehabilitation needed help. Moreover, my age and experience would be an asset instead of a liability as it might have been in other fields. My goal was solid and not just a pipe dream. No one could cause me to get sidetracked.

I remember the psychiatrist's reaction to my stated goal of becoming a counselor. He threw his pencil up in the air and as it landed on his desk, he said, "Mr. Staccia, why don't you choose a goal that is possible!" His reply to my statement of wanting to help mankind was, "How about womankind also?" I was discouraged after my conversation with the psychiatrist. Maybe he could see something I couldn't. Remembering how wrong he had been previously caused my motivation to return, however.

Going to college seemed almost impossible. Everyone at the halfway house where I worked as a volunteer counselor was encouraging. The opportunity was there because the Veterans Administration had changed my Bad Conduct Discharge to an Honorable and I was now eligible for the G.I. Bill. In fact, I was already receiving compensation from the V.A. because my ex-wife encouraged me to seek their help. She was very supportive throughout my recovery process and continues to be my best friend today.

My next move was to find a college that would accept not only an eighteen year old GED, but also a prospective thirty-seven year old student who had neither attended one day of high school nor sat in class for twenty-two years. It wasn't easy. The admissions counselor at the local private school barely contained himself as he told me how the university received only the top ten percent of the high school seniors nationwide. He suggested the local junior college whose admissions person suggested that I return to the local high school and "take some night courses first". Finally, the admissions person at Urbana College, Urbana, Ohio, said, "Mr. Staccia, I will call your bluff. You will be admitted here on two conditions. First, you must show ability to do college level work which will be determined by a *C* or better grade on your course work. Secondly, the V.A. must agree to pay. If both of the above requirements are not met by quarter's end, you may forget your involvement here with no obligations." It was immediately agreed to and I entered Urbana College in June, 1974. Eighteen months later, I graduated with a Bachelor of Arts degree in Social/Psychology with honors and had already started my Masters program at Wright State University in Dayton, Ohio.

In 1977, I graduated from Wright State University with two Masters Degrees, one in Rehabilitation Counseling of the Severly Disabled and the other in Mental Health Counseling. I went to work for the State of Ohio as a Rehabilitation Counselor for the Bureau of Vocational Rehabilitation in Toledo, Ohio. Although having virtually my choice of about fifteen cities within Ohio to work, I chose the city of Toledo. They didn't know it yet, but the University of Toledo had been selected as the school for my doctoral work. It had the best combination of counseling and psychology in the state, according to my estimation. First, I had to work for a year and save my money since the V.A. would not pay for a Ph.D.

Thanks to Professor Robert E. Higgins, I entered the University of Toledo as a full time student in October of 1978 on a graduate assistantship. I finished my course work for the Ph.D. a little over a year later and took six months to write the dissertation. Dissertations are never accepted on first submission, however, and mine was no exception. I did my internship at Community Hospital, Springfield, Ohio, beginning in March, 1980, while rewriting my dissertation. A year and a million rewrites later, my dissertation was completed and I took my Ph.D. on June 6, 1981.

My mother's eyes would always shine with pride as she introduced me as, "My son, the Doctor". It was a long distance from the sadness reflecting from them as I stumbled upon the porch in my drinking days. I thank God that Mom lived to see me sober up and become stable.

My experience as a psychotherapist concentrating in the area of alcoholism rehabilitation covers more than ten years. I remained at the halfway house for three years, worked for the State of Ohio for a year and The University of Toledo for two years. This latter position included not only counseling the student with alcohol problems, but also serving on the committee to eliminate problem drinking. My doctoral internship was done at Community Hospital, Springfield, Ohio, wher I remained for three and one-half years.

Finally, I worked at Madison County Hospital, London, Ohio, one year before entering private practice in January, 1984.

I have written many papers on alcoholism and lectured virtually all over the state of Ohio at universities, workshops and counselor conventions. Views on my theory of alcoholism causation and treatment, which was the topic of my Doctoral dissertation, were presented to a national audience in Baltimore, Maryland, in 1983. My theories were also presented at a statewide conference of counselors in Columbus, Ohio, in 1984. Finally, I served as vice chariman of the board governing alsoholism counselor certification for the State of Ohio in 1983.

I am now a stabel alcoholic and thank God for the opportunity to have been able to say that daily for more than ten years. It is a day at a time effort, but the results are beautiful. Life is wonderful and it is great to be alive. I hope you enjoy this book, but most of all, I hope it assists you with whatever alcoholism problem with which you are confronted. God bless you!

CHAPTER ONE

UNDERSTANDING ALCOHOLISM

The reader might find this chapter the most informative and useful work on alcohol and alcoholism ever read. Not only myths of drinking are dispelled within this chapter, but also issues relative to the thinking which motivates the alcoholic are examined. Some of the myths of alcoholism behavior are examined in such a way that the reader is invited to "get inside the mind" of the alcoholic for it is reasoned that one cannot understand an alcoholic otherwise.

It is virtually impossible for a person who is not alcoholic to fully understand from an internal frame of reference the alcoholic's motivation or how his mind functions. Questions asked within my practice relative to alcoholism invariably center around these two issues. Questions such as, "Why did he do that; is he crazy?" or, "Why can't he at least call me; doesn't he care?" are heard daily. These and similar questions are difficult to answer adequately. This is especially true for the non-alcoholic person who just doesn't know how the alcoholic thinks or feels.

An attempt will be made, however, to convey this to the reader.

The difficulty in understanding alcoholism from an internal frame of reference by a non-alcoholic is monumental. The difficulty might be better understood by using an example. Suppose we tried to teach a man or virgin female what it's like to be pregnant. Any mother might say, "That's easy. It is like . . . Well, it's more like . . . Oh, you know what it's like." Obviously, it is not easy to explain such a complex phenomenon to anyone having not experienced pregnancy. Although we can acquire knowledge relative to carrying and giving birth to a child, only a mother can truly realize this experience from an internal frame of reference. We can come close to that realization by study and observation. The closer one comes to having a full internal frame of reference with any experience, the better one's understanding of it will be. This is especially true with alcoholism.

Therefore, the significant other will come closest to understanding the alcoholic only through studying valid subject matter and relating it to themselves. In other words, every alcoholic is an individual with many similar characteristics allowing us a baseline with which to understand them. Rest assured that after finishing this chapter, you will have a better realization of what it means to be an alcoholic than ever before. Do not despair, however, if after reading this chapter, your knowledge of alcoholism is still lacking. For reasons already given, it may be physically impossible for you to ever completely understand an alcoholic unless you are one.

There has been alcohol and those who use and abuse it since long before recorded history. It is estimated that drinking of ethyl alcohol for religious and ceremonial purposes predates all forms of religious writings by thousands of years. Since the recording of such history, it seeems that all religions speak against the evils of intoxication. Many, in fact, strictly forbid its usage and ban the perpetrator to eternal hell. On the other hand, various religions continue to use alcohol within their ceremonies as a *spiritual lubricant.*

Could it be that the alcoholic is attempting to gain a closer relationship with God by indulging in the forbidden nector? After all, at one time it was reserved only for the clergy and their dissemination of the fluid. No. That would be all too simple an explanation. The alcoholic does not drink for any planned outcome, but only because he is compelled to do so. He is sick. This is evidenced by the fact that the alcoholic continues to drink even after he knows it is destroying him and his loved ones. Why, then, does an alcoholic drink and, more importantly for this chapter, what is an alcoholic?

Very simply put, if you have *any* problem that is a direct result of drinking alcohol and you continue to drink then you are an alcoholic. Notice the emphasis on the word "any". In defining the term alcoholic, the size or seriousness of the problem is not a factor. The problem, for example, might be that you continually make a fool of yourself at parties or get-togethers where alcohol is served. Maybe you only miss a few days work every month due to drinking the night before you are scheduled to work. It might be that you continually do things while intoxicated that violate your moral code or value system. On the other hand, the problem might be as serious as having committed murder or vehicular homicide while under the influence. Once again, if there is *any* problem either caused by alcohol or increased in severity by alcohol (ulcers, etc.), and you continue to drink after the alcohol-problem connection is made, then you are alcoholic.

Another indicator of alcoholism, second only to the above alcohol-problem connection, is the loss of control concept. Loss of control occurs when the drinker consumes more alcohol than intended, whether in number of beers, shots of whiskey, or glasses of wine. One might, for example, have intentions of *two or three* and actually drink several. This, in turn, might trigger a drinking bout lasting an evening, weekend, or longer. The alcoholic will invariably be guilty of stopping for *only one before dinner* and actually drink until the wee hours, not only missing dinner, but much more as well.

The American Medical Association used about three and a half typewritten pages and the World Health Organization more than five to define alcoholism. Such lengthy definitions, in my opinion, tend to confuse the issue and cause a comparison process by which the one suspected of being alcoholic can eliminate himself. The person caught up in this process will say, "I have this or that symptom, but I don't have that one." The progression of this type of thinking invariably leads to a conclusion of "not alcoholic" by many persons who are.

In fact, the alcoholic will see and hear all evidence indicating his "normal" state. Conversely, he will deny by not seeing or hearing any evidence confirming his alcoholism. This is not a conscious process, but one in which the alcoholic actually indulges in self-deceivement. Through a complicated psychological denial system (see glossary), the alcoholic becomes totally dishonest unto himself. This type of reality distortion and selective reasoning is not only understandable, but also predictable, especially when one truly understands how the alcoholic thinks. The bottom line is that the alcoholic will be the very last to see and accept evidence of his own alcoholism. In other words, the alcoholic actually distorts reality to confirm his innocence. He will invariably add to this self-deceit process by not drinking for periods of time which might last days or weeks. He or she will purposefully deny drinks at parties and comment to everyone how Pepsi tastes better than bourbon. After a while, however, an "incident" will occur in which a deserving drink is taken. A gradual or abrupt return to old drinking habits will then be justified. More of this self-dishonesty concept will be discussed later on in this chapter and at length in the chapter on treatment.

Intensifying the problem of self-deceit are myths of alcohol which the alcoholic interprets in a way that will prove, once again, his innocence. The significant other might also be deceived by these myths. One such belief is that alcohol acts as a truth serum and allows the real person to emerge. Nothing could be further from the truth. Alcohol virtually distorts the thinking process. It is equivalent to throwing a liquid "monkey wrench" into the mental machinery that prevents us from acting on impulse. This monkey wrench can be seen as the intoxicating effect of alcohol. As a result, the intoxicated person is caused to make decisions based on alcohol reasoning. These decisions invariably not only conflict with social rules, but also violate the moral code and value system of the individual.

We all have a certain self-disciplining and restraining quality within the brain which I refer to as **mental brakes**. Mental brakes actually stop us from doing things that pop into our minds from time to time. It might be making a pass at a fellow worker or neighbor whom we know to be married, or stealing a little something from a department store. Too much alcohol releases these mental brakes and should not be seen as the individual's logical planning to engage in uncharacteristic or unsocial behaviors. As we all have impulses to indulge in socially unacceptable behavior at one time or another, mental brakes prevent us from doing so.

The intoxicated person, however, invariably does not have this braking mechanism. Moreover, the alcohol adds further to the problem by complicating the thinking process. This causes even further anti-social thoughts which have no resistance to actual performance. It is totally incorrect to assume that an intoxicated person is capable of rational planning or thinking. He or she, however, is capable of performing behavior based on thought patterns already stored. Such behavior results not from intent or what is really desirious of the individual, but because the brakes are removed by the intoxicating effect of the alcohol.

It is important to point out a fundamental difference between this

concept of mental brake release behavior and what I refer to as
sober pre-planned alcohol-excuse behavior. The person who uses
alcohol as an excuse to indulge in certain behavior falls within this
latter category. He or she will indulge in sober, pre-planned, alcohol-excuse behavior. An example of alcohol-excuse behavior can
best be realized through the following scenario. Joe or Jan has been
watching the next door neighbor with a lustful eye for sometime. An
opportunity presents itself when the neighbor's spouse goes away
for a week. Joe or Jan then arranges for their spouse to visit a
relative who lives out of town and will require at least a weekend
visit. The stage is set. Joe or Jan will proceed to get intoxicated and
make overt advances toward the neighbor next door. If the plan
backfires, then the excuse will be "I drank too much and really
remember nothing about the entire incident. The last thing remembered was drinking because of missing my spouse terribly and being
very lonely. I must have gone next door just to visit, etc." Variations
of this theme are many, but I believe the point is made.

It is sometimes very difficult to determine whether the behavior is
of the first or second type. Clues can usually be found by examining
an individual's drinking history and his or her quickness to use
alcohol as an excuse. Let's assume, for example, that the person
described within the preceeding scenario already had a history of
infidelity, flirting or playing around. Also, he usually drank very
little and rarely got drunk. This appears to be a case of using alcohol to excuse pre-planned behavior. On the other hand, the person's
history of drinking might have had an alcohol-problem history already established. Moreover, he or she was not one to cheat or be
promiscuous. This might very well be a case of alcoholic behavior
and not alcohol-excuse drinking.

In the first example, the alcohol was used as an excuse for pre-
planned behavior. In addition, this person had no history of an
alcohol-problem connection. Alcoholism could be developing here
but is unlikely the blame for his infidelity. This is because of the
specific nature of his behavior. Alcoholism behavior is not discrimi-
nating and is erratic. It will cause the drinker to do all sorts of
bizarre things while under the influence. Infidelity was used because
it is the alcohol problem seen most often within my practice. On the
other hand, alcohol might just bring to light a relationship or marriage problem and, of course, is treated accordingly.

Without belaboring the point, one other factor needs mentioning
within this discussion. The alcoholic will invariably defend erratic
behavior through means other than alcohol. This is because of the

need to deny any problem with drinking. The alcoholic will condemn drinking and make the alcohol-problem behavior connection when all else fails. He will do it then only long enough to get through a particular crisis. Conversely, the excuse drinker will immediately focus on alcohol as the villain that caused the problem.

A myth of alcoholism is that the alcoholic drinks because he or she wants to. If true, it would also follow that the alcoholic could stop drinking at will. The alcoholic wants to believe this because it affords him a means in which to avoid the realization that he has no control over alcohol. The alcoholic thus convinces himself and others that drinking is fun and a desirable part of life. Statements such as, "I can quit anytime I want to," are heard daily in the counseling room, as well as in the family living room.

My answer is always the same. "Excellent! Since alcohol is causing you very serious problems, why not quit today?" After such an exchange, the client and I invariably will go through a process of bargaining in which he agrees to give up the alcohol. When he fails, the bargaining continues. This time, he agrees to being admitted to an inpatient treatment program if the drinking doesn't stop. In other words, he has displayed a lack of control and is obviously unable to quit on his own. Therefore, a controlled atmosphere is necessary and inpatient treatment is indicated. This will allow him a period of time in which the drinking syndrome can be broken. Invariably, clients will not succeed in quitting on the first attempt. This is true although they could not be more sincere during the bargaining process.

The alcoholic will defend his inability to quit with statements such as, "It is silly to deprive oneself of something so enjoyable," or, "It was a stupid agreement in the first place." Nevertheless, I make the client stick to the bargain. Of course, this technique of treatment will be discussed more extensively within chapter three, but is cited here to illustrate my position that alcoholics are not capable of controlled usage. They drink because they have to, even though they might pretend to self and others that it is by choice.

The reader might counter with, "But no one is holding a gun to his or her head to make the individual drink." This is true, but there is a connection between alcohol and the alcoholic so strong that such an example might be useful. Let's say a gun were arranged in such a way that it would go off when the alcoholic took another drink. Further, let's say the gun was pointed directly at the alcoholic. I think you would hear not only the echo of gun shots around the world, but also emergency squad sirens as well. In essence, the alcoholic is playing with a loaded gun, and long after he or she knows it, continues to do so.

In my own drinking history, especially in the latter stages, there were times that I wanted to control my drinking but couldn't. My frustration and helpless feelings were so strong that I have actually cursed the bottle before drinking from it. But long after realizing that my control of alcohol was lost, I still convinced others and frequently myself that it would be easy to quit and my drinking was strictly by choice.

The myth that is absurd, even to the alcoholic but prevalent among both laymen and professionals alike, is that the alcoholic drinks to have fun. Only someone who has never experienced the agonies of alcoholism can make such a statement. In defense of such naive thinking, it might be fair to point out that from outward appearances, the alcoholic is having fun. This seems true, at least in the early stages of the disease. Most alcoholics will agree that a certain amount of fun was experienced in their early involvement with alcohol, yet that same person, having gained stability within his life, will also admit that such fun was far lacking in quality. In fact, most recovering alcoholics will deny it was fun when compared with their present concept of fun and enjoyment.

It is true that the alcoholic actually involved himself physically in dancing, romancing and partying during the time he drank. His emotional involvement and appreciation for the experience, however, was lacking. These same activities provide such a superior quality of enjoyment and fun to the stable alcoholic that it is unbelievable until experienced. My stable clients never tire of sharing this one aspect of recovery with me.

The stable alcoholic can "party" with much more intensity and sensitivity while absorbing emotional stimuli from others and also sharing likewise. There is such a different meaning to the word "party" when one becomes stable. Hearing a using alcoholic describe his drunken behavior as "partying" upsets me like fingernails scraping on a chalk board. For the using alcoholic, the party is over and it has been over for quite some time. Any "fun" garnered from alcohol when taken by the alcoholic is strictly that of the spectator who watches the idiotic, drunken antics.

Another version of this is the professional or layman who believes that the alcoholic drinks to feel good. Hogwash! The alcoholic never feels really good whether drunk or sober. There might be periods when the alcoholic feels a lack of pain. Actually, the alcohol has numbed the nervous system and, comparatively speaking, he feels good. This can be compared to the type of good feeling one might experience when he stops beating his head against a wall. Essentially, the drinking alcoholic's feelings are in a state of suspended animation. In this state, his real emotions, thoughts, and feelings are shielded from reality. These concepts will be discussed at length within chapter three. After reading it, you will probably agree that the alcoholic definitely does not drink to have fun or to feel good.

Since man took his first drink of alcohol there probably have been myths and misunderstandings about its effect on the human organism. These false beliefs relative to the effect that alcohol has on the mind, body, emotions and behavior are still rife today. One would suppose that a society capable of going to the moon and having a cancer cure right around the corner could accurately identify the effect of alcohol on the user. It is possible to do so, but the false beliefs still prevail.

You are probably becoming more aware of how this misunderstanding complicates alcoholism rehabilitation. As you continue reading, try using your own imagination. I am sure your understanding of the complexity of the problem will be much improved. You will see, for example, how these *old wives tales* contribute to the initial or further use of alcohol by some and an inaccurate appraisal of the results of their usage by others. The overall result of this ignorance, in my opinion, complicates the rehabilitation of the alcoholic and his family.

It is difficult to successfully rehabilitate those suffering from alcoholism until we break down the false belief system that tends to support the disease. This means that all too much time is spent in dispelling the myths and misunderstandings relative to the chemical, yet it must be done. If, for example, one views alcohol as an aphrodisiac (sex stimulant), then it is more difficult to convince him not to drink. In addition, it becomes more difficult for a family member to be forgiving of some idiotic statement made by the intoxicated person if alcohol is seen as a truth serum. We now continue with more myths of alcohol in general and not necessarily those of alcoholism, per se. My comments will be minimal and made primarily relative to alcoholism.

Myth: "One cannot become alcoholic who drinks only beer." This is just not true. Ethyl alcohol is present in beer (brewed), wine (fermented) and whiskey (distilled) and is exactly the same. Only the concentration is different. In other words, there is approximately one ounce of ethanol in a bottle of beer (12 oz.), glass of wine (6 oz.) or shot of 100 proof whiskey (3/4 oz.). Notice that the concentration of alcohol is more intense relative to the process of establishing alcohol within the liquid. Distillation, or whiskey making, causes the highest concentration. The reason one can drink more beer than whiskey without getting intoxicated is obvious. That doesn't mean that one alcoholic beverage is any less harmful, alcoholically speaking, than another. In fact, I have treated many a "beer only" alcoholic.

Myth: "A drunk person tells what's been on his mind or always the truth." This is really absurd. Yet, many a spouse, child, etc., of an alcoholic invariably needs to be convinced that a drunk is essentially out of his mind. The chemical reacts the brain in such a way that causes absolute and total confusion. This confusion is not selective. Even though the drunk invariably can not spell his own name, the spouse will often be devastated when the drunk makes such statements as, "I never did love you"

Myth: "A female can not drink as much as a male without getting drunk." This is not true. It all depends on body weight (see appendix). Intoxication occurs as a result of blood alcohol content and is accurately predictable. As the alcohol level within a given blood volume increases, the intoxicating effect also dramatically rises. Therefore, a 160 pound person, male or female, will be affected equally, all other factors (food in stomach, etc.) being equal.

Myth: "Alcohol is a stimulant and every outdoorsman should carry a flask just in case he is over-exposed to the cold." Absolutely wrong. Alcohol is a depressant or "downer" in street terminology (see appendix). This myth is probably kept alive by the fact that alcohol intake appears to stimulate the drinker for two reasons. First, it lowers one's inhibitions, thereby causing the person to become more outgoing. A shy person will become more socially active and will dance, talk and generally interact with others at an above normal pace. It is as if the person gained strength and energy from the drink. Of course, the capacity to interact was always there, but due to shyness, remained dormant until after inhibitions were lowered by the alcohol.

Secondly, alcohol actually does have a brief stimulating effect on the organism. This is because of the irritating effect it has on mucus membranes of the mouth, esophagus and stomach walls. The body actually attempts to compensate for the shock of irritation by a generalized reaction. There is an increased heart and respiration activity, elevated blood pressure and temporary increase in mental activity. This initial reaction to alcohol is brief. It lasts about five to thirty minutes with the first drink and even less with each additional drink. Following this brief stimulation, alcohol's depressing action returns. This myth can be especially dangerous to one exposed to extreme cold temperatures. When extremities are in danger of frost bite, or worse, the alcohol will numb one's sensitivity to the cold, thereby interfering with corrective action.

Myth: "All alcoholics are bums." The skid row person so often visualized by the public as the typical alcoholic makes up less than five percent of our population. Alcoholism has no socio-economic favorites. It also does not discriminate by race, color or religion. Alcoholism is present among professionals, blue collar workers and laborers of all kinds, as well as the unemployed.

This myth promotes alcoholism by giving one a false sense of security about drinking. It is reasoned by the drinker and others, for example, that unless one is jobless and a gutter bum, his drinking is harmless. The beginning alcoholic further reasons that even if he has a *little trouble* with alcohol, he works and takes care of his family and certainly is not alcoholic. The fact is, eighty percent of all alcoholics work and a high percentage of them are professionals.

Myth: "I don't drink every day, therefore, I am not an alcoholic." Actually, the daily drinking alcoholic is of a minority within our ranks. Most alcoholics drink only on the weekends. Many are even more periodic with their drinking and some are occasional alcoholics. By this last statement, I mean the person who drinks only on occasions when his drinking is accepted and in this way, he attempts to make it right. Anniversaries of all kinds, holidays, promotions, deaths, etc., are all examples of experiences when the occasional alcoholic will have problems.

In my estimation, there are almost as many types of alcoholics as there are drinkers. We actually promote alcoholism by identifying only certain types of behavior or drinking as being alcoholic. This allows the alcoholic who is in a denial state, which includes just about every untreated alcoholic, more escapes. He can pick apart all the behavioral characteristics presented as being alcoholic and accurately deny that he is "that way". He will find something about every symptom or characteristic that is not him. "I don't do this or that," is a typical statement of the denying alcoholic.

Myth: "Alcohol in a hot toddy prevents or cures the common cold." If this were true, I personally would never have had a cold. Depending on what other ingredients are contained within the *toddy*, this statement is absolutely false. The depressant and general numbing of the senses caused by alcohol will help one better tolerate the cold's miseries. Alcohol, however, has no healing quality either for the common cold or any other illness. However, it can be used as an antiseptic in most cases if poured directly on the cut or laceration.

This myth contributed to my own continued drinking. The only time I felt comfortable drinking at home after my problem was identified was when down with a cold. During those times, my wife would fix me a hot toddy or two, or three. Each succeeding toddy would contain more whiskey and less of the other "junk". These colds would be extended as long as possible and would sometimes require many fifths of whiskey to "cure".

If you believed any of the previous myths, you need more education within the area of alcohol and alcoholism. If you use any of the excuses presented below in order to drink or if you have one of your own, then you might be prone to alcoholism. Social drinkers do not need reasons to drink and they do not make excuses for doing so. Following are a few less popular myths of alcohol and more excuses to drink given by alcoholics in my office daily.

I really enjoy drinking.
I need a "couple" to relax.
My wife, husband or kids drive me crazy.
A little whiskey is healthy; it helps the heart.
People say I'm easier to be with when I've had a few.
A shot of whiskey stimulates the blood on a cold day.
When I'm nervous, a few drinks will calm me down.
I deserve a drink after a hard day's work!
Alcoholism is just a lack of willpower.
I don't drink much. People must be lying!
Alcohol relaxes me.
Alcoholism is a weakness of the mind and spirit.
I drink because. . . .
I can quit anytime.
At least I don't take any drugs!
Et cetera, et cetera, et cetera.

Facts of alcohol are a little less humorous. Many of them are presented herein. This section is further divided into sub-sections of informative facts about beer, wine, and whiskey respectively. Once again, I apologize to the reader who does not enjoy this type of "dry" reading. It is deemed necessary, however, for your continuing education on the subject of ethyl alcohol and alcoholism. These facts are culled from tons of literature, seminars, workshops, and my own experience. It is not meant to be a complete work since that could take volumes in itself. Discussions of specific alcoholic beverages will be preceded by a general information statement about alcohol.

Ethyl Alcohol (C_2H_5OH) is the main intoxicating agent in beer, wine, and whiskey. It is also referred to as beverage alcohol. Medical literature classifies beverage alcohol as "an addictive narcotic-like substance". The World Health Organization lists it in the same category with codeine, morphine, cocaine, opium, heroin and all other addicting narcotics. Medical authorities in the fields of pharmacology and toxicology also classify beverage alcohol as a drug. Accordingly, alcohol is seen as an anesthetic, a hypnotic, an analgesic, a poison, a depressant, an irritant and a sedative.

The term alcohol is derived from the old Arabic word "Al-kohl" meaning a fine cosmetic powder. The word assumed different meanings over the years. "The most subtle part of anything," seemed to be the closest definition translatable into English. Around the 19th century, the word alcohol was used to describe the content of wine. Today, alcohol is commonly used when discussing both ethyl and methyl alcohol. The latter, methyl alcohol, is commonly referred to as wood alcohol and is poisonous.

Ethyl alcohol is defined as a clear, colorless liquid having a rather insignificant odor and causing a burning sensation in the mouth, esophagus, and stomach. It can be produced by fermenting sugars such as molasses and fruits, or starches as in grain and potatoes. Often, ethyl alcohol is *denatured* for industrial use by the addition of chemicals such as camphor or benzenes which would render it unfit for human consumption. Further, ethyl alcohol is classified by the proof number which is double the percent of alcohol by volume per gallon. Thus, a "90 proof" whiskey contains 45 percent alcohol by volume. Wines generally are 16 to 40 proof (8 to 20 percent alcohol) and beers are from 4 to 12 proof (2 to 6 percent alcohol).

Alcohol cannot be rightfully called a food. Although it does supply calories of energy, they are empty calories. Alcohol contains no vitamins, proteins or minerals, and its dominant properties place it among the dangerous drugs. Alcohol is one of the rare chemicals that enters the bloodstream in its undigested form. This is accomplished by osmosis through the mouth, esophagus and stomach membrane linings. Its primary entry into the bloodstream (80%) is by absorption from the small intestines. The effects of alcohol in the bloodstream arise from anesthetic properties of alcohol. As a drug, it produces progressively depressing action on the central nervous system similar to that of ether and chloroform.

The fourth most common disease in the United States, alcoholism contributes to a death rate which ranks third among all other fatalities. Death occurs from acute over-ingestion of alcohol, cirrhosis of the liver, suicide, and highway accidents incurred while drunk. Also, acute withdrawal states accompanied by delirium tremens (DT's) often result in death. In addition, rehabilitation facilities and agencies are innundated with clients suffering from impairments related to alcohol causation. Chronic disabilities, such as organic brain changes, result directly from drinking and render the alcoholic a permanent mental invalid. Moreover, a staggering number of persons are recovering from spinal cord injuries and other severe disabilities due to automobile accidents, gunshot wounds, and other alcohol-related accidents. The rehabilitation cost alone to the taxpayer runs in to the billions yearly.

BEER: THE BREWED BEVERAGE

Brewers of beer the world over use special techniques and additives to make their product more appetizing and appealing to the consumer. Although such practice contributes greatly to the damaging effects of the chemical, brewers continue doing it, especially in Canada and the United States. Extremely damaging whether synthetic or organic, both types of additives are used, a few of which are presented herein for the reader's edification.

Gum arabic (Acacia plant) is used by many breweries as a stabilizer to prevent alteration of the chemical components of the beverage during storage and prior to being sold. It also helps the foaming quality of the beer. The American Medical Association warns that *allergic reactions*, liver and kidney damage may follow the use of gum arabic. Other additives such as dextrin are also used for this purpose. Dextrin is a white amorphous powder used by brewers to insure a better head of frothy bubbles on the surface of the beer. Dextrin is also used in the manufacturing of matches, fireworks, and explosives.

Many additives are used for *cosmetic* effect only. Sodium hydrosulfite, which is a white or grayish white salt of hydrosulfurous acid, is used in industry as a reducing and bleaching agent. As a beer additive, it prevents the beer from developing a caustic taste and prevents a generalized deterioration of flavor. In addition, cobalt is used by some breweries to prevent overfoaming even though it has been linked directly to cardio-vascular complications. Federal officials in the United States and Canada have strongly implicated cobalt as not only causing death in some instances, but also directly causing many other serious cases of beer drinkers' heart disease. In this illness, the heart muscles of the beer drinker slowly degenerate and finally stop working.

Another cosmetic additive used by breweries is tannic acid which is a yellowish to light brown substance used in tanning, dyeing and the manufacturing of ink. Taken internally, it can be blamed for arresting secretion, causing contraction of the tissues and arresting the flow of blood within the vessels. Tannic acid has been known to cause gastric irritation and liver damage. Disregarding these dangers, many breweries use it to eliminate cloudiness from their brands of beer caused by sediment action.

Similarly, tartaric acid is used. It is a colorless or translucent chemical used in photography and for silvering mirrors and coloring metals. It is occasionally used in medicine as a laxative. Because some batches of beer are so cloudy and unappetizing no one would drink them, brewers add tartaric acid. Once again, this eliminates the cloudiness and presents an appetizing appearance.

Ironically, some additives such as ammonium phosphate and magnesium sulfate, are used by brewers for opposite reasons, especially when the product is for export. Although ammonia phosphate has many uses in industry such as fireproofing fabrics, fertilizer, preventing after-glow in matches, and as flux for soldering tin, copper and brass, beer companies use it to chemically change American water. This is done so the water in the beer will correspond with the water used in European brewing although we hear and know that most water in Europe is tainted, and American water is generally much cleaner and purer.

In addition, magnesium sulfate (better known as Epsom salts) is a cathartic or purgative. It is the active ingredient in most of the advertised laxative waters. Breweries rely on Epsom salts to alter water used in brewing. They ignore medical warnings that excessive use can cause respiratory failure and kidney impairment.

Of course, additives are used for more practical reasons. Papain (papayotin), for example, is a chemical additive akin to meat tenderizer which prevents beer from clotting. In medicine it is used as a solvent for warts and other external skin growths. Any internal use carries with it the warning that certain individuals may exhibit severe gastro-intestinal symptoms after ingestion, yet this chemical substance is widely used in brewing.

Beer always contains the narcotic lupulin. Its history and chemical breakdown are interesting. For at least 1200 years, hops have been used to impart a bitter flavor to beer and malt liquor. We have all heard the word "hop" as a slang term for "dope" or a narcotic drug such as opium. We have also referred to persons intoxicated with a narcotic as "hopped up". The chemical breakdown of lupulin would provide an interesting correlation between beer and marijuana. It, however, is not within the scope of this book to enter into such a discussion. The interested person is once again referred to my previously cited doctoral thesis.

If this information causes you to be alarmed, it might further interest you to know that as of 1985 there is no law governing the ingredients of alcoholic beverages. If a brewer wished, he could add many dangerous chemicals other than those mentioned above to his brew and not break the law. More astounding is that the average drinker is kept in the dark as to what goes into his body when he drinks beer. Yet, all foods sold within our supermarkets must have a content label.

Of course, alcoholic beverages are governed by the Bureau of Alcohol, Tobacco and Firearms, not the Federal Food and Drug Administration. There is presently a battle raging within the judicial system as to whether we, the consumer, should be apprised of what we are drinking. If the consumer advocate wins, there will be a label required on all alcoholic beverage containers. It will have to list content information, including all additives. We should recieve a ruling sometime in 1986. It is my guess that many drinkers will reconsider the "innocence" of having a drink or two after reading that label.

WINE: THE FERMENTED BEVERAGE

Wine is a moderate alcoholic beverage made from the juice of fresh, ripe grapes. Wine can also be made from the juice of many fruits and plants, including apples, cherries, and dandelions, but the word *wine* most often refers to the beverage made from grapes. Natural fermentation usualy yields an eight to twelve percent of alcoholic content which is found in some of the better, natural wines. Many wineries, especially in the United States, add various types of distilled spirits to raise the alcohol percentage. Other synthetic chemicals are added, especially in the United States, to cause various results such as those mentioned in the section on beer.

Wine experts classify wine in many ways. Some group wines by the country that makes them. Others list wines by generic and varietal names. Most people who produce and use wines divide them into six main classes according to when the wines are generally served. The six main classes of wine are: 1) appetizer wines, 2) red table wines, 3) rose' (pink) table wines, 4) white table wines, 5) dessert wines, and 6) sparkling wines. Wine producers base these classifications on commonly accepted ideas of when the wines are served.

A good rule of thumb to follow when selecting a good wine is to look at the alcohol content, country of origin, and date of bottling. As stated in the previous section, we should soon have content labels on all alcoholic beverages. At that time, one will be able to make his selection rather easily. Just look for the bottle with the least additives. Just grape with natural fermentation would be excellent depending on your taste as to white, red, etc.

WHISKEY: THE DISTILLED BEVERAGE

Whiskey is a strong alcoholic beverage made from such grains as barley, corn, rye and wheat by a process called distilling. Distillation raises the alcoholic content because alcohol has a lower boiling point than water. Distillers first grind the grain and cook it in water, forming a mash. Then they mix in malt, which changes the starch in the grain into sugar. Next, yeast is added and the mixture ferments. Fermentation changes the sugar to ethyl alcohol. The mash is then heated, giving off alcohol vapors (remember alcohol boils at a lower temperature than water). Distillers collect the vapors (which is alcohol) and cool them. When cool, the vapors liquefy as whiskey. Before distillers bottle the whiskey, they add distilled water, diluting most beverages to between 80 and 100 proof.

Whiskeys differ according to the grain used, the proof of the beverage, and the aging time. The most common U.S. whiskeys are blended whiskey, Kentucky bourbon, Tennessee whiskey and rye. Blended whiskey is at least 20 percent straight whiskey, blended with other whiskeys or with pure ethyl alcohol and water. Kentucky bourbon is made from a mash of mostly corn. Tennessee whiskey is similar to bourbon, but is filtered through charcoal before aging. Rye is made from a mash of mostly rye grains. Any U.S. whiskey except blended whiskey may be labeled "bottled in bond" if it has aged at least four years and is not less than 100 proof.

Imported whiskeys come primarily from Canada, Ireland and Scotland, but we virtually import from all over. Canadian whiskey is a blend usually made from corn and rye, with some wheat and barley malt. Irish and Scotch whiskies are made mostly from barley.

Scotch whiskey tastes smoky because it is made from malt that has been dried over peat fires. Russian vodka is usually made from potatoes to form the mash and then distilled to at least eighty proof. Certain types of vodka are raised to one hundred proof alcohol. Rum is imported primarily from the Caribbean Islands (Puerto Rico) and South American countries. It is made from molasses with a special distillation process. The alcoholic content can range from eighty to over one hundred proof. Finally, tequila is a Mexican product made from agave, a cactus-like plant, and can also range from eighty to over one hundred proof.

I hope these facts were not too boring. It is hoped that you found them interesting. They will be useful. If you want to see a content label on alcoholic beverage containers, you can help. Please write your congressman just a short note telling him of your desire. Personally, I hope the label will already be in place as you read this but somehow, I doubt it.

In returning to our discussion, there are many more myths and facts of alcohol and alcoholism, but I believe, a sufficient number of both have been presented. The above information should have enlightened the reader about alcoholic beverages. Hopefully, this information will help you better understand the alcoholic and the complexities associated with the disease. It should be sufficiently clear by this time that the person who contributes most to the perpetuation of myths and denies facts the most is the alcoholic, himself.

It is important that the reader understand that the alcoholic's readiness to keep these myths alive and facts suppressed is motivated by his denial system. In fairness to the alcoholic, however, it seems far fetched to imagine that the average person suffering from alcoholism has as much knowledge on the subject as you, the reader, now have. And we've only just begun.

As your knowledge base about alcoholism improves, a better understanding of the alcoholic is sure to follow. You might read the prologue of this book again at this time. It will help you to get inside the mind of an alcoholic. Let your preconceptions about the disease rest while you read the prologue. Try to visualize what it must have been like to be as caught up as I was in alcoholism and not know it. Be aware that a very thumb-nail sketch of myself was presented. Left out are hundreds of episodes of drinking, manipulations and con games.

The person manipulated, lied to and conned most, however, is always the alcoholic himself. This is done through his own denial system. I firmly believe that the using alcoholic is incapable of being honest because of this self-deceit. It is like a color blind person trying to convince you and himself what a peacock really looks like, color-wise. The reason significant others have such difficulty *pinning* the alcoholic down is because of this self-deceit resulting from alcoholism.

An example of this type mental phenomenon might be helpful. Some of you might recall a statement by Mr. DeSalvo, otherwise known as The Boston Strangler, who engaged in sex crimes during the 1960's in Boston. The Boston police confessed that their inability to make any prediction about the next scene of the crime complicated their ability to apprehend DeSalvo. Mr. DeSalvo later admitted to the police that he, himself, had no idea that he was going to commit a crime until ten or fifteen minutes prior to its commission. "Often times," he said, "I would be on my way to work or taking a lunch break or just driving around when the urge would occur." He had no idea who his next victim would be or where she lived. So, too, is the using alcoholic as difficult to predict because the thinking processes are quite similar as far as being random and unpredictable.

The times I got drunk after having started to work or was on lunch break or going to the store, etc., are too numerous to list. My "honest" intentions were to have one beer or drink, but I would wind up drunk for a day or weeks at a time. Often, it frustrated me as much as it did others. The jobs lost as a result of such irresponsibility are also too numerous to mention. My wife was upset the most when I did such crazy things. She and the kids took it personally as if they were the reason for my staying out late or not coming home at all. It is true that I didn't want them to see me in a drunken, sorry state and often times drove around or sat in a bar until they were in bed. The drinking, however, was not related to them at all.

My drinking bouts started, often as not, for no apparent reason. The thought would just pop into my head and once started, there was no control. That is alcoholism. Please don't interpret this as excuse making. That is the farthest reason in my mind for stressing this concept. It is essential that significant others understand this aspect of alcoholism for their own benefit and recovery effort. It will help eliminate your feelings of rejection and unworthiness to know that the alcoholic does not plan their behavior because of those around him or her. On the contrary, awareness of the feelings of anyone else or their reaction to the alcoholic behavior is farthest from the using alcoholic's *mind*.

A bull in a china shop concept might be the best example I can use to convey this to the reader. If one can visualize those who are closest to the alcoholic as being the fine china lined up nice and neat on shelves of the china shop and the alcoholic seen as a bull just trying to find an exit. He first just bumps into objects of fine crystal and china knocking them to the floor accidentally, but breaking them just the same. The longer the bull is trapped and is unsuccessful at getting out, the more scared and desperate he becomes. Finally, he is thrashing, breaking and creating havoc while destroying everything in his path.

The alcoholic is like the bull and the family, friends, and relatives much like the china. Alcoholism can be compared to the china shop itself while the alcoholic can be seen as trapped inside and often trying to get out. First he or she just bumps into loved ones; they crack; they hurt. Later the destruction is much worse and the hurt unbearable. When you feel that it is impossible to be hurt again because no feelings are left, you are proven wrong. Much of this is self-imposed, however, because non-alcoholics simply give the using alcoholic too much credit for being a sane and responsible person, both of which he is not. Significant other damage is briefly covered here in order that the reader gain a better understanding of alcoholics. We do damage to everyone around us, almost always without intending to do so and very often without realizing it. The significant others have difficulty with this concept because their hurt is real and they internalize and take it personal. The significant other is justified in thinking this way and very commonly states, "Even a fool should be able to see it." Yes, even a fool could see it. But we are more than just fools when we drink, because we are alcoholic.

Once again, although it sounds like I am making excuses for the disruptive behavior of the alcoholic, nothing could be further from the truth. In fact, any effort to come between the alcoholic and the full negative impact of his behavior is what I call supporting his or her alcoholism. Before leaving this subject, I feel it necessary to mention that an alcoholic should be confronted about his disruptive behavior. This will help him in recognizing his disease. On the other hand, it is important neither to be caught up in addressing the behavior as if it were intentional nor to take it personally. This is difficult, I know, but must be done. We must not lose sight of the real culprit which is alcoholism.

If we become entangled in the behavior and focus too dramatically on it, we might begin to view alcohol as a symptom of the behavior. This leads to the often heard statements that he or she drinks because of some type of frustration or dissatisfaction with job, neighbor, spouse, etc. We begin to make excuses for the alcoholic with this type of thinking. It is extremely important in dealings with alcoholism that we see alcohol as the cause for disruptive behavior and not vice versa.

"an alcoholic's subconscious wish"

In your eyes it is clear
that you believe my lies;
do not to us do this, dear,
but destroy my disguise
.....D.A.S....

CHAPTER TWO

ALCOHOLISM CAUSATION

In treating alcoholism, counselors generally agree that any time spent between therapist and client in seeking the cause of alcoholism is wasted. Instead, we usually ask the client not to waste such valuable time searching for the answer as to why they drink, but to apply that effort toward rehabilitating from its damage. This approach is effective with most alcoholics, but there are those of us who can't seem to be satisfied so easily. We need to at least exhaust all efforts toward trying to determine what caused our problem. Only then will we concentrate our full effort toward its cure.

This chapter is dedicated to those who are seeking the elusive answer to the unanswerable questions, "What causes alcoholism?" or, for that matter, "Why did we start drinking in the first place?" Within this chapter, we will review causative factors and analyze some of the more prevalent theories of alcoholism. First, I must be fair with the reader. As of this writing, there is no definite known cause of alcoholism unless we simply say too much alcohol causes alcoholism.

Although my doctoral thesis was based on my theory of alcohol-

ism, I would be less than honest if I said it is the only cause. My theory, which will be presented within this chapter, is valid and accounts for one's use of alcohol to cope with self-felt pressures of society. In my opinion, once one uses alcohol for this or any purpose other than social drinking, he or she is on the path toward alcoholism. This is true especially when one accepts the false promise that alcohol will get one over society's hurdles unscathed. After reading this chapter, I am sure you will agree that alcohol causes alcoholism and the question once again is, "Why does one drink alcohol in the first place?"

Theories of alcoholism causation usually address one of three factors of the human organism: physical, mental or social. If we look closely, each theory will make sense and, therefore, depending on your leanings, will be the one most acceptable to satisfy your curiosity. Keep in mind, however, that alcoholism attacks the entire human organism, i.e., physical, emotional, spiritual, social and mental. This is true regardless of which theory of causation you find most acceptable.

Those who believe that alcoholism causation is due to physical factors put forward tons of data substantiating the body's reaction to various aspects of ethyl alcohol usage. Usually with a medical background, these theorists will talk excessively about the body's reaction to alcohol and the body cells' adaptation to it. Lengthy discussions are presented relative to the metabolic process (how alcohol is burned up or converted to harmless chemicals or waste within the body). Also, they will talk of the brain's need for sugar and the need that nerve endings have to be anesthetized (put to sleep).

The more popular physical theory of alcoholism causation is that alcoholics are genetically predisposed to be alcohol abusers. Simply stated, this means that because of some gene transmitted through the family tree, our systems are prone to alcoholism. This, the genetic predisposition theory, holds that there is a physical weakness relative to alcohol which has been handed down from an alcoholic parent or grandparent.

Another area in which many theories of alcoholism causation are derived is social. The theorist who sees peer pressure, parental influence, television commercials or any type of need to conform accepts social causation. In other words, society, itself, is the cause of alcoholism. Many social learning theories have validity. If we, for example, drink because our friends or relatives drink, then we are

learning to drink because we see their behavior as worthy of emulation.

Although belonging in the overall area of social causative factors for alcoholism, the theory of peer pressure is somewhat different than that just described. One who drinks to be accepted by his or her peers may not necessarily perceive drinking as a positive trait. Such a person drinks because highly-regarded friends or relatives do, but indulges only to be accepted by that particular group. The peer pressured individual may or may not perceive individuals within the group as having desirable characteristics worthy of emulation. Drinking for this population becomes a passport to group acceptance and is not necessarily internalized. This is unlike the emulators previously mentioned who want to be like Dad or Aunt Susan. Furthermore, those who drink for peer or group acceptance might even view alcohol as distasteful. They might find alcohol undesirable when the need for acceptance no longer exists or when separate from the group. This type of alcoholic is seen often in the treatment setting. It is not unusual to hear statements like, "I would pour my beer out when no one was watching," or, "I would act drunk in order to be like the others."

Those who are "faddish" and follow media influence might be highly susceptible to this type of drinking. Television commercials and other media advertisements usually attract these individuals. Because they are so easily swayed, however, their preference might change from the latest alcoholic beverage to plain carbonated soda if media so dictates. In other words, there is no strong attraction to the chemical, *per se.*

Therefore, one who drinks for this reason might have a better chance at recovery as they lose respect for the peer group. It is important to point out, however, that many of these faddish type drinkers do become severely addicted to alcohol and require an extensive effort to rehabilitate. Unfortunately, there is no way of predicting who will become alcoholic as a result of this social pressure type drinking and who will not. It's a risky gamble at best. Many more variations of societal causative factors for alcoholism exist and, as with all theories of causation, make sense when closely analyzed.

We now turn our attention to an area of the human organism which is seen by many theorists as a leading cause of alcoholism. It is the human mind, or psychological component of the body. The word psychology means study of the mind. The term *psychological deprivation* (see glossary) used within this chapter denotes that the person is deprived of some psychological functioning or adjustment to society. Although closely related, it is separate from what is normally considered physical or social. In looking at psychological reasons for drinking, we examine the extremes.

There are those who drink, for example, in order to quell a slight nervousness prior to toasting the bride and groom. On the other extreme, however, are those who drink in order that "Martians" won't be able to control their thoughts. Those who fall within this latter category are at the extreme edge of psychological deprivation. They are generally considered mentally ill and disturbed. These individuals are rarely aware of the relationship they have with alcohol. For reasons which will be explained later, alcohol actually contributes to their functioning within society at a higher level of acceptability than possible without it. This is partially due to society's reluctance to accept *abnormal* behavior, yet willingness to accept alcohol as a valid excuse for it. The person who talks to himself while under the influence, for example, is better tolerated by society than the one who does so while sober. It is also partially due to the fact that alcohol does suppress or mask certain forms of mental illness. Why and how this takes place will be explained shortly. For now, suffice it to say that the problem becomes even more complicated because of this "masking" effect. This is especially true when identifying and treating alcoholism resulting from mental illness.

Counselors and other health professionals invariably miss a fine point when alcohol is not the primary problem, yet conceals the actual problem. This is a rare type of alcoholism which is caused by the underlying mental illness, and is definitely secondary to it. You will recall that within the prologue, I talked about how certain health care professionals, i.e., psychiatrists, treat alcoholism as if it were a symptom of another problem.

In the type of alcoholism just described, they would be correct. Consequently, the alcoholism might even cease to exist after successful treatment of the mental illness. This, as a matter of fact, explains their treatment approach to the problem. Therefore, psychiatrists who view alcoholism as a secondary problem to mental instability are justified in this particular instance. This particular aspect of alcohol related mental illness will be discussed in detail within chapter three. Presently, we are looking at psychological deprivation as a causative factor.

In review, the term "psychological deprivation" refers to mental rather than physical reasons seen as alcoholism causation. In viewing the extremes, we discovered that there might even be times when

alcoholism is not an appropriate primary diagnosis. We might find that alcohol is actually *covering up* psychological deprivation which we can safely term as mental illness. An example of this might be the individual bothered by voices within telling him or her to do something terrible or immoral. The voices might suggest that the person is a thief, a liar, a child molester or an undesirable bent on dastardly acts. The voices might direct him to do something harmful to self and/or others, or that another is intent on harming him.

An accidental relationship might be established between the person experiencing the "voices" and alcohol. As a result of the alcohol's influence, the voices might change their messages to a more acceptable type of persuasion or disappear altogether. This person might then continue using alcohol in order to control the perceived voices. He would exhibit all signs and symptoms of alcoholism, but would not be primarily alcoholic. In this case, alcohol is being used to suppress or eliminate symptoms of a severe psychological condition technically referred to as paranoid schizophrenia. Alcoholism would be secondary to the mental illness.

Another example of alcohol usage preventing serious psychological problems from emerging is one in which the individual might exhibit an explosive type of personality. He might even be potentially dangerous to self or others. Through alcohol, which is a sedative, destructive impulses are not so intense and self-control is more easily managed. In order to maintain normal behavior and some form of control, these individuals might rely so heavily on alcohol that they become alcoholic or, in some cases, at least appear to be. Ironically, just the opposite is generally true of non mentally ill persons. In other words, alcohol will cause normal mental processes to deviate toward abnormality.

Of course, the psychological or personality problems re-emerge after removal of the alcohol. I have treated alcoholics with very similar type symptoms within my practice. In most cases, alcoholism was secondary to the mental illness. Often, very little effort is necessary to rehabilitate this population from alcoholism once the underlying problem is successfully treated. This extreme has been presented to illustrate how alcoholism can result through prolonged usage by individuals on the extreme edge of psychological deprivation. It is, therefore, seen as a causative factor.

For those involved in less severe types of psychological deprivation, it is just as serious, but is usually nothing more than a perceptual problem. This means that the individual is just not using his faculties to see things clearly. This is contrary to the previous individual who did not have the faculties. Within the psychological deprivation theory of alcoholism causation, we consider all aspects of perceived weaknesses. One might drink to mask certain perceived physical inadequacies. People indulging for this reason might, while under the influence, perceive themselves taller, prettier, heavier, lighter, etc. In other words, an individual drinks to change himself into being a more self-perceived, desirable person. Because of the strong social factor, we will call this area of alcoholism causation *psycho/social*. Moreover, the term *psycho/social deprivation* (see glossary) will be used to mean that the person is deprived in both the psychological (probably minimal) and social interaction areas. Prior to further discussion on this, however, let's review some of the information presented thus far on alcoholism causation.

Although alcoholism causation is unknown to us at this time, we can, and do, advance theories as to its causation. No one theory is valid enough that we can say definitely that alcoholism is caused by . . . We can say, however, that prolonged excessive use of alcohol will cause one to eventually be alcoholic.

Immediately, the reader might ask, "What is *excessive use*?" The answer to this question is simple. One who uses alcohol for any but social purposes is using alcohol excessively. Social purpose is defined as the use of alcohol to stimulate the appetite prior to a meal. It also means to have a glass of wine with one's meal or just to accommodate a host or hostess at a party.

More specifically, excessive use is defined as the use of alcohol for a reduction of tension, stress or any feeling of inadequacy. Further, it is the use of alcohol for reduction of physical pain of any kind and psychological pain of all kinds. Finally, excessive use of alcohol is a personal issue, is different in each individual and can not be measured by quantity or frequency alone. In other words, alcohol usage to cope with life in any way is viewed as excessive and sets the stage for alcoholism.

In returning to our discussion, my theory of causation is now presented. Basically, I believe the pre-alcoholic uses alcohol to cope with a normal type of anxiety which is present in all experiences. (The term "anxiety" will be defined shortly). Further, I believe that this artificial reduction of anxiety not only impairs the individual's normal coping methods, but also sets up a dependency link between alcohol and anxiety which eventually develops into alcoholism. Consequently, the individual ceases to develop in many social and psychological areas. This causes a developmental gap which will remain until the drinking stops and a return to normal coping meth-

ods is realized. This latter concept is explained in detail within the chapter three.

The relationship between alcohol and anxiety reduction is not new although many theorists believe the opposite relationship exists. In other words, they believe that alcohol usage conditions the body in such a way that anxiety results from alcohol withdrawal. This is a valid theory, but occurs mostly in the later stages of alcoholism. We are presently concerned with the very beginning stages, however, and will look at only the alcohol-anxiety reduction aspect of this relationship. The uniqueness of my theory lies in the acceptance of a certain type of anxiety and the belief that this type of anxiety is normal. It is necessary to define anxiety and present my views on a particular type of anxiety.

The acceptance of my theory is based on the assumption of two major tenets or beliefs. First, that alcohol will reduce anxiety, and secondly, that a particular type of anxiety is normal. It might be helpful for one's acceptance of my theory to understand these two basic principles. The former assumption will probably meet with very little resistance from the reader. The latter assumption, however, might be more difficult to accept because even the lay person believes anxiety to be damaging and an undesirable trait. But what is anxiety? We hear this word often enough, but few laymen are familiar with its complete definition. Most correctly believe it to be a fear, but it is a particular kind of fear. It is a fear from within rather than a fear from without.

A fear from without is easily recognizable and has some definite, visible source. For example, the fear of being dog bitten, the fear of a bridge collapsing, or the fear of crossing a busy street are visible fears. On the other hand, an inward fear has no visible, definitely recognizable source. For example, one might enter a room full of people and, for no apparent reason, develop symptoms of an inner fear. This is anxiety. The symptoms of both inward and outward fear are quite similar. Some of the more recognizable of these symptoms are an increase in heart rate, sweaty palms and underarms, generalized weakness, shortness of breath, and an urge to run. Quite simply, if one exhibits any or all of these symptoms with no apparent physical threat, then one is experiencing anxiety.

According to my theory, anxiety not only is normal at times, but also experienced by everyone at varying levels of intensity. In fact, a complete absence of anxiety while socially interacting is undesirable and only possible under certain conditions. There are also different types of anxiety, one of which I call **Experiential Primal Anxiety**

(EPA). This type of anxiety is completely normal and is usually at its highest intensity when we are confronted with a new experience. Any experience not actually done before will cause *Experiential* (experience) *Primal* (first time) *Anxiety*, abbreviated EPA.

This EPA type of fear from within, or anxiety, will be present each and every time we experience a particular event (such as dancing). Moreover, it will be present at varying degrees of intensity. EPA will be highest the first time we experience the event and lowest when we are most comfortable or familiar with it. For example, the first time we went to school, was called on by the teacher, danced, kissed, or made love, we experienced high levels of EPA. It is present for each and every experience with the intensity levels ranging from low to high depending on the situation.

We might, for example, have low EPA relative to dancing, but high EPA for public speaking. We could have both at the same special event, such as a fund raiser. You might, for example, be called on to speak and later be expected to dance with your date or spouse. Your EPA might be a one (range zero to seven) for speaking and a five for dancing. This would indicate that you are more comfortable with talking to a crowd than dancing. Finally, we will continue experiencing EPA the rest of our lives, unless, of course, we never do anything new or different. The EPA will either be at a high, moderate or low level of intensity.

As indicated, Experiential Primal Anxiety is completely normal and harmless when viewed as such, but can be socially crippling. It is also one of the primary contributors to alcoholism causation if the relationship between EPA reduction and alcohol is made. The alcoholism causation connection will be made shortly, but first a little more ground work. When EPA is at a high level, one is very uncomfortable and will take action to reduce it. Depending on whether one sees the EPA as normal or not will determine one's reduction strategy. An example of EPA reduction can be best illustrated in the following scenario. It is one in which a sixteen year old youth is confronted with an initial dance experience.

The youth walks into a dance hall and is overwhelmed with EPA. He might recognize the crowd as being familiar and friendly, but the activity in which they are engaged is threatening. Couples are dancing and swinging to the beat of a band playing at least two decibels higher than normal. The surrounding atmosphere is new either because of the decorations or the individual has not been there before. More importantly, he has never danced before.

This experience is totally new to the young person and his EPA

level is probably seven. Remember that EPA is measured on a scale of one to seven with one being low and seven being high. A crucial decision is made at this time by the dancer as to whether his symptoms, i.e., elevated heart rate, sweatiness, shortness of breath and generalized weakness, are normal or abnormal. He decides that they are normal because neither has he been here before, nor has he danced before. He, therefore, decides to continue the experience even though the urge to run is strong. In other words, he remains at the dance and, more importantly, he dances. As a result of this decision his EPA will reduce normally and will be somewhat lower (possibly a five) the next time he is confronted with a dance experience. After several such experiences, the EPA will be significantly reduced from the first time of the experience. No developmental gap (see glossary) will be present in the future for this individual relative to dancing. He has developed normally with a natural reduction of EPA. (see appendix)

On the other hand, if a decision had been made that the EPA intensity of seven was abnormal, a completely different outcome would have occurred. With the thought that the EPA was abnormal, the individual might have panicked. His thoughts might have been, "What's wrong with me? Everyone else seems to be doing fine, but I feel like I am going to die." With this reaction, the individual would take avoidance action in order to reduce the anxiety. Avoidance could be accomplished at least two ways. The first way is flight, which is our initial reaction to panic. In this way, the individual might reduce his anxiety through physical avoidance. In other words, he pretends to be sick or remembers a serious problem at home and leaves the dance. The second way in which to avoid the anxiety is to choose psychological avoidance through the use of alcohol. The former method is rather self-explanatory; the individual's anxiety reduces automatically when he or she leaves the anxiety producing situation. The latter method of anxiety reduction, however, needs further explanation.

Let's suppose the individual decided to leave (flight being one's initial impulse when confronted with EPA) and he met a friend with some form of alcoholic beverage who persuaded him to partake of it. Immediately after the first drink, his anxiety level would begin to drop. Further drinking would cause a continual dramatic reduction in EPA until it eventually reached zero. This would be due to the alcohol-anxiety reduction relationship mentioned earlier. It would happen quickly and completely. The individual's sickness suddenly disappears and the important business at home can now wait while he returns to the dance floor and dances.

Unlike the person in the first example, however, this individual's EPA will not reduce through normal confrontation. In fact, it was probably zero throughout the evening because of the anxiety reduction effect of the alcohol. Furthermore, because he didn't confront the EPA head on but elected to lean on a "crutch", its reduction was not worked through and his EPA level will be at seven the next time he goes dancing. He knows how to eliminate such uncomfortable feelings, however, and proceeds to drink again thereby reducing his EPA level to zero. Of course, he will experience the same high level of EPA at the next dance and once again will use the same coping mechanism which is alcohol. Even though this person is physically experiencing the dancing activity, he is not reducing his EPA by confrontation, but is avoiding it altogether.

This causes a developmental gap for dancing. He will always experience high EPA relative to dancing until he works through the EPA. At age thirty, he might react to dancing like a sixteen year old (with anxiety). This is the developmental gap. Because of the alcohol-EPA reduction relationship established, he will probably continue this coping method in other EPA provoking situations. Of course, since EPA is present in all new experiences, it is conceivable that this individual will eventually be either an alcoholic or a social isolate. In either event, he will more than likely have a generalized developmental gap that will cause him serious problems in later life. It will also require extensive therapy coupled with meaningful effort from the individual to close.

A developmental gap can occur without using alcohol to avoid EPA, but we see it almost one hundred percent of the time in treating the alcoholic. In my opinion, this gap accounts for the immaturity we see in older recovering alcoholics. It is not unusual in therapy, for example, to hear a thirty-seven year old adult actually reasoning on a sixteen year old's level. As the developmental gap closes and the client reaches a higher level of rehabilitation, he can't believe the things he said at an earlier stage of his recovery. This type of immature behavior at earlier stages of recovery are the rule rather than the exception.

I have yet to treat an alcoholic who did not exhibit many or all of the characteristics of the EPA theory. The theory also has a recovery component in which all the previous concepts are not only elaborated upon, but also applied to the rehabilitation process. This will be covered in depth within chapter three.

For now, the reader should begin to realize that the developmental gap is a serious impairment to one's daily social functioning. It should also be clear that the alcoholic's rehabilitation is definitely a social process. Moreover, the developmental gap can only be closed through experiencing all of the EPA producing events in a sober and confrontive way after recovery begins. It is my belief that one is not fully recovered until one can experience, in a completely sober state, the things that one has been avoiding through alcohol. That is not to say that he should do them all, but just be able to.

In concluding this chapter on alcoholism causation, it must be restated that we do not know what causes alcoholism. Certain basic theories were discussed, including social learning, biological and hereditary concepts. Also, my theory on causation was presented. A strong statement, with which I believe all theorists will agree, was made. Briefly, that statement is that alcohol ultimately causes alcoholism! No matter why one begins to drink, if one drinks excessively long enough, one will become alcoholic. The Chinese proverb "Man takes a drink; the drink takes a drink; then the drink takes the man," seems very true, indeed.

CHAPTER THREE

TREATMENT OF ALCOHOLISM

This is my favorite chapter because writing about treatment and recovery of alcoholism brightens me considerably. My spirits are uplifted by thoughts of those I've seen turn their lives around. As the treatment aspect of this disease unfolds throughout this chapter, you, too, will gain optimism. Rest assured that it will not be a false optimism, but one rooted in reality. After completing this chapter, I am sure you will agree that alcoholism can be successfully treated. Laymen and professionals alike will appreciate the step by step, simplistic way in which this truth is brought to light.

In my estimation, even the most severe alcoholic cases are far from hopeless. This optimistic outlook not only is imperative for counselors, but also must be conveyed to the alcoholic. How can we expect the alcoholic to believe in his recovery if we don't have hope and confidence in his ability to get well? My confidence is reinforced almost daily as I see alcoholics recover. Often, this is after others have given up on them.

My own recovery probably gives me hope in this area because of the seemingly helpless, hopeless person that my alcoholism caused me to eventually become. Everyone seemed to have given up and accepted that I would never be anything but a drunken bum. I was about to give up on myself when something or someone awakened a small thread of hope within me. That small thread provided just enough strength to keep me from complete destruction. The thread of hope grew stronger and was eventually woven into a strong net. With this, I was able to climb from the cesspool of alcoholism and back to a normal life. It wasn't easy giving up the alcohol and it took strength that I thought was lost. Fortunately, it was still there, although well hidden. This little bit of strength gave me hope. From hope comes strength and strength regenerates hope.

There is a thread of hope, however microscopic, to which every alcoholic alive clings. The essence of treating the alcoholic, therefore, is helping him to realize this thread of hope. We must then hang on to him until he has strength enough to hang on to it himself. The prologue will help you accept that no alcoholic alive is beyond or incapable of recovery.

A word of caution about treatment. Although the ultimate responsibility for recovery rests with the alcoholic, the counselor plays a major role. It is important, therefore, that one use a critical examination process when selecting a counselor. Examine his or her credentials with the utmost care. Do this as if you were selecting a brain surgeon, for in a sense you are. Determine if earned degrees are from accredited universities and within the field of counseling, social work, psychology, or a closely related field. In addition, be sure the counselor is credentialed to treat alcoholism.

While on this subject, I must make a strong statement directed primarily to the counselor. It concerns the client's dignity which, of course, should never be violated. Although all reputable counselors know this, there are those claiming to be counselors who don't. These so-called counselors bully, badger, demean and embarrass the client within group settings. They do this to the extent of tearing away what little self-respect and essence of self (the thread) the alcoholic has remaining. In the name of counseling, these fools also carry this type of stupidity outside the group setting. They make the client carry a red pillow of enormous size, for example, if the client is not expressing anger. He is made to carry this through the cafeteria, to AA meetings, etc. He might even be required to carry more than one such pillow representing other unexpressed emotions. They might also require the client to wear a gag if the client isn't talking enough in group. Another such *trick* is to require a client to wear a sign around his neck. Stupid statements such as, "I am a fish

because I am hooked,' are seen on these signs. It infuriates me to think of such absolute asininity.

This type "counseling" is not recommended or condoned by any professional person or organization within the counseling field. The people who do this or any similar activity in the name of counseling should be severely reprimanded if not fired on the spot. Invariably, these "counselors" are recovering individuals who are still very sick themselves. Moreover, they often do not have an educational background in counseling. Usually, they are ventilating their own sicknesses at the client's expense and should be avoided. Nowhere, but nowhere, in counseling ethics is such practice condoned.

In addition, the field of alcoholism counseling is rife with "do gooders" who are ready to tell you what to do. Every recovering alcoholic, for example, prides himself as a counselor of those with less sobriety time. Certain Alcoholics Anonymous (AA) chapters are inundated with what I refer to as "Coffee Cup Counselors" (see glossary), whose *counseling* should be avoided or taken with a grain of salt. There is no doubt that AA is an indispensable asset to the recovering alcoholic, but one should avoid being "counseled" there. Those who would attempt counseling at AA meetings are well-meaning, but dangerous. To be a licensed professional counselor requires at least a Masters degree, one year of supervision, and three years of experience in most states. Unless your counselor has a similar background, view him or her with caution and skepticism.

Although adding to one's overall qualifications to counsel alcoholism, being alcoholic is certainly not the only qualification. The old saying that the best alcoholism counselor is a Ph.D. alcoholic with at least five years sobriety is true. The question arises, however, as to what is more important, being alcoholic or having counseling credentials? In my opinion, alcoholics are people who have normal problems as well as alcohol complications. Alcoholism, of course, is the primary problem and must be treated first. Many of the underlying problems, such as work, marital, etc., will clear up automatically with sobriety and regained stability. Very often, however, there are serious complications lying dormant underneath the alcoholism. These require expert counseling skills to help the client work through. Therefore, an alcoholism counselor must be fully qualified to do general counseling as well.

The typical alcoholic coming into treatment is angry. He is there because of a court order, an angry boss, a frustrated spouse or a bleeding ulcer. Invariably, a crisis precipitated his admission, such as a DWI (driving while intoxicated), a D&D (drunk and disorderly), a domestic violence charge, a threatened divorce suit, and/or threatened loss of job. He is sick, sad, sober and sorry, but worst of all, he is cut off from his supply of alcohol.

The alcoholic is angry all right and why shouldn't he be? Here he is in a forced relationship with a bunch of no good drunken bums. Surely, he doesn't belong here. My goodness, he has a job and family, money in the bank and can quit drinking anytime he wants to, or so he thinks. Of course, he thinks this way. Otherwise, he wouldn't be in treatment.

What does alcoholism treatment consist of? Well, there are two basic approaches to the treatment of alcoholism and they are not necessarily exclusive of one another. One is the outpatient approach in which the alcoholic remains at home and sees a counselor on a regular basis. This is done while continuing his daily activities including work, family and social obligations. A very in depth plan of treatment is written for not only the alcoholic, but also his entire family. In fact, treatment of non-drinking or non-alcoholic family members is so important that there is an entire chapter on that subject immediately following this one.

The second basic approach to treatment is inpatient. This usually consists of admitting the alcoholic to a controlled atmosphere located adjacent to or within an acute care hospital. There the alcoholic receives medical attention, if needed, along with medical tests of various organs suspected of being damaged due to alcohol. Inpatient treatment can be five days to three months in length depending on the program. Contact with the outside world is limited, including family visitation. The alcoholic usually volunteers for such treatment and is free to leave at any time.

Successful outpatient treatment is extremely difficult even if the alcoholic is motivated toward recovery. Old habits are hard to break and, worst of all, old drinking buddies are difficult to dispense with. Furthermore, the pressures seen by the alcoholic as a cause for his drinking (wife, job, neighbors, etc.) are still present. While we know these things are not "causing" him to drink, the alcoholic truly believes that they are. It must be remembered that the alcoholic has used drink to cope with every type and level of frustration, i.e., anger, anxiety, and all emotional stress for such a long period of time that his coping impulses automatically revert to drink. Moreover, the alcoholic has probably never learned coping skills for any type of social interaction. He may be twenty-five or thirty years old chronologically, but only sixteen or less emotionally and psychologically. This is the developmental gap we talked about in the previous chapter.

Further complicating outpatient treatment is that the alcoholic is going through a physical and psychological withdrawal from the chemical, a process which is horrendous. As the chemical leaves the body, the entire nervous system undergoes a shock. Nerves that were previously put to sleep by the chemical begin to awake. They experience a bombardment of noise, light and human interaction of an intensity not felt for some time. This causes further withdrawal symptoms of anxiety and awakens old fears of dying, going crazy, etc., and causes a generalized inability to perform daily tasks. All sources of instability are exaggerated and impact upon the alcoholic all at once.

Added to this is usually the feeling of being treated for the wrong thing or that the wrong person is being treated. The alcoholic in this stage of recovery invariably is not only denying his alcoholism, but also blaming others for his dilemma. The wife, boss, neighbor, etc., are seen as the source of his problems and he believes that one or all of them should be talking with the "shrink". So the first step toward treating the alcoholic on an outpatient basis is education, education, and education. If you can keep him sober long enough for him to learn something about alcoholism and to apply it to himself, there is a chance for recovery.

The early stage recovering alcoholic is almost impossible to educate for two primary reasons. First, within every alcoholic is a very strong denial system which converts real information about alcohol into a false reality. The alcoholic can repeat everything he has ever heard about the positive qualities of alcohol, i.e., that it stimulates the appetite, aids digestion, and is an excellent tranquilizer. Invariably, one will hear such statements as, "Even Jesus Christ took wine at the last supper," coming from the early stage recovering alcoholic. Conversely, he distorts or blocks out all information that would reflect its dangerous effects. Moreover, he will give reasonable explanations for all his problems without ever including alcohol as a possible cause for any of them.

It is important to remember that the alcoholic's denial system is totally subconscious. That is, he is not consciously aware of the process of deceivement occuring within; he actually believes his own lies. This, too, is part of the denial system. In fact, the dishonesty that is so prevalent with the alcoholic is primarily a dishonesty unto himself. He really believes what he says and will go to any lengths in order not to recognize alcohol as his problem. I have seen alcoholics, for example, exhibit psychotic-like behavior (which means crazy acting) rather than let alcohol take the blame for their irresponsible behavior.

The alcoholic's denial system is so strong that he will divorce his wife (because she is the problem), quit his job (because it is the problem) and move to another state (because the rut here is the problem) rather than confront the real problem which is alcohol. Of course, he thinks problems such as those mentioned are real and denies seeing them as just symptoms. Specifically, the alcoholic's denial system will do anything and everything in order to shield the alcoholic's conscious mind from the truth. The alcoholic is just not conscious of his developing alcoholism or what it entails. This is all part of the denial process. A further explanation of a denial system in general, and of an alcoholic's in particular, might be helpful. We all deny certain things. Our waist line is getting larger (the laundry shrunk my clothes); we were too lazy to mow the grass (my aunt Matilda stopped over); or we didn't want to buy a birthday present or take someone to dinner (oh my gosh, I forgot). If we take our denial system and multiply that times ten, we have the denial system of an alcoholic.

Denial is a subconscious process to keep certain types of information from reaching the conscious mind. This is because it must be acted on at the conscious level or result in guilt feelings. Because there is a pleasure center of the brain (see appendix) that desires to be tranquilized by alcohol, the alcoholic's denial system works overtime. Yes, there is definitely a component of the brain that actually fights against recovery. This component will be discussed in detail during the discussion on relapse within this chapter.

How does one break through such a denial system? First of all, the therapist must be able to communicate with the alcoholic in such a way that a mutual understanding and trust is established. Secondly, it is important to continually dwell upon alcohol as the primary problem no matter how much the alcoholic attempts to sidetrack into other issues. The alcoholic will lead a merry chase and, very convincingly, explain how his job situation, family situation, etc., is just too intolerable for any human to withstand. My patented reply to such statements is, "Have you ever tried not drinking for a while and see if the situation might be more manageable?"

By bringing the focus back to alcohol, I attempt to establish a *bargaining* situation. If successful, an agreement will be reached in which all drinking or use of other drugs, including prescribed tranquilizers, will cease. Usually, the bargain will be struck for whatever time he will agree to. If he says he can quit drinking for a month, I ask him to prove it. If he wants to bet that he can go for six months without a drink, I will take the bet. The object is to do whatever is necessary to bring attention to the drinking and cause it to stop. This might sound like the alcoholic is being set up to fail, and he is. More accurately, his denial system is being set up for failure. When the alcoholic perceives reality in regard to this "control" issue, his denial system fails. As stated, his denial system is very strong at this time, and sometimes the only way to penetrate it is to help him see how little control he has over his drinking. If the alcoholic is incapable of keeping his end of the bargain even for a day, it brings more light on his helplessness over alcohol. Therefore, treatment-wise, he wins and denial fails. Moreover, as a result of this *failure*, we have something tangible with which to confront the alcoholic.

By continually bringing the focus back on his inability to quit, even for a week, month, etc., the alcoholic must eventually confront his loss of control (see glossary). Furthermore, I will bargain in the direction of inpatient treatment if we can't break the usage cycle or if outside influence is too overwhelming. Usually, a deal is made that if he or she can not stop drinking completely by a specified time, then we will agree to inpatient treatment.

If the drinking stops, however, the client is signed to a contract (see appendix) that clearly delineates what is expected during the outpatient treatment program. This same treatment approach is used with appropriate modifications for inpatient. In order to better clarify this treatment program, an imaginary person called John Smith and his family are used for illustration purposes.

After contract signing, an individualized written treatment program is designed for John. This treatment program will include the entire family, his boss, real friends and all significant others. Education is the primary thrust at first along with individual, group and family therapy sessions. Within the educational effort (attended by all those closely associated with the alcoholic), I stress the need to see alcoholism as a disease. It is stressed that alcoholism should not be viewed with any more stigma than that of having diabetes. Through slides, lecture and role play, the development and progression of alcoholism is presented. All, and especially John, are made to see how John's entire personality has changed as a result of the chemical.

The family is made to see how they are victims of the disease and how they, themselves, through ignorance, have supported the alcoholic's disease. The boss, as well, has played a role in supporting this crippling progressive disease of alcoholism. Invariably, significant others are not aware of their roles in supporting John's alcoholism. Notice that I use the word *support* and not *enable* which is a popular word for significant other involvement with the alcoholic. I find **support** to be a much more accurate term in describing the role of significant others and I explain it fully in chapter five. For now realize that *support* does not imply the same family responsibility for drinking that *enable* does.

Systematically, it is shown in vivid detail how alcohol caused John to act contrary to his moral code and value system while under its influence. All too often, we tend to lose sight of the fact that an alcoholic has a value system and moral code. We take for granted, for example, that he is acting under his own convictions when he cheats on his wife, steals from his friends, or lies to his boss. Nothing could be further from the truth. He, invariably, is as ashamed of such behavior as the clergyman down the street would be. The difference is that the alcoholic will not allow himself to feel the psychological pain resulting from his behavior while under the influence of alcohol.

Further, it is related how the behavior just described was probably mild in the early stages of drinking compared to the later stages. At first, John, while under the influence, might have only winked at the boss's wife while at a party. Later, however, as his disease progressed, he might have been so bold as to pinch another man's wife and try to make a date with her. Finally, in the later stages of his disease, John's behavior grew to be even more bizarre and socially damaging. He did things that caused his family and friends to be embarrassed for him while he apparently felt no remorse. Worse yet, John continued doing more despicable things while violating his own moral code and value system. All the while, it might have appeared as if John were truly immune to the social shame he was bringing upon himself and family. Actually, John was immune, but through the insulation of alcohol.

You see, every time John felt shame or fear or any emotion for what he had done while under the influence, he drank to cover it up. As indicated, these value violations were relatively minimal at first and were probably excused by a catch all statement such as, "I was tipsy," followed by nervous laughter. As his alcoholism progressed, John's denial system became stronger and he stopped admitting that he drank too much. To do so would be admitting that alcohol was a problem. More importantly, to do so would mean that he must stop drinking. Yes, John's denial system is working well and he is drinking to cover up his feelings. In other words, rather than feel the full impact of the psychological pain (feelings of guilt, shame, fear, etc.), John drinks alcohol which in turn causes the feelings to be suppressed.

As his feelings are suppressed, John builds a defensive wall (see appendix) around them. This wall not only shields John from his own feelings relative to violating his moral code and value system, but also shields his real feelings from his family and loved ones. The wall becomes so thick that John does not seem to feel remorse about anything he does. To "bluff" his way through and give the appearance of being okay, John develops a phony behavior which reflects just the opposite of what he is really feeling. His real feelings, of course, are not conscious even to him.

This phony behavior assumes many forms. John appears to be a big man, number one, really having it all together and an all around decent guy. He actually begins to believe his own lies and accepts himself as being a very important person. He may even evaluate those around him, using his own perceived self-importance as a yardstick. He begins to doubt that his wife is worthy of him, his job good enough or the town worthy of his presence. This distortion of reality becomes so real to John that he convinces others who, in turn, begin to see and accept themselves relative to John's perception of them. The wife and family develop a form of neurosis (mild mental disorder) in which they see themselves as John perceives them. The reader should begin seeing more clearly why the entire family is in need of therapy.

Group therapy is an invaluable aid in the recovery process. I know of no more effective or quicker way to break through John's defensive wall and denial system than with group therapy. We use this method to help John gain a deeper knowledge of the concepts being presented within the educational process. More importantly, it better enables John to internalize them. Through the group therapy process, John begins not only to understand these concepts, but also to bring them to bear on himself and, as much as possible, impact upon his emotional system. As the group experience continues and John becomes more involved, he, invariably, will want a private session of individual therapy. This is in order to share his newly emerging feelings with someone perceived as less threatening than those within the group.

Depending on John's psychological stability, I might accommodate him, but only sparingly. Individual therapy might be necessary for John to put himself back together well enough to *tell it* in group. In my estimation, very little recovery is accomplished in private sessions. As you will see later, complete rehabilitation of the alcoholic is impossible in the individual or private therapy session. According to my treatment theory, individual therapy, for the alcoholic, is just preparation for group therapy and group therapy is just preparation for the social world.

The theory behind group therapy is simple. The entire group gets well together. Through active participation either physically or through active observation, each group member experiences one another's healing process. As one person works through a traumatic past event, for example, all group members share that experience. They do this by relating to the person experiencing the event. Thereby, they, themselves, come closer to working through their own difficulties. In other words, the combined input of group members contributes to the overall recovery process of each individual member within the group. Moreover, as one person breaks through his or her wall of defense, others do likewise for the realization that others are experiencing similar difficulties is therapeutical in itself. Finally, it is estimated that the healing potential of a group is greater than the combined number within it. A group of seven, for example, has the healing potential of eight or more.

Ideally, the group size is eight, including the counselor, but can vary two or three people either way. More than eleven group members detracts from the effectiveness of the group and it becomes a mob with too much input for a facilitator (group leader) to manage therapeutically. Conversely, a group of less than five members does not have enough input to stimulate the entire group. It then becomes a sewing circle with usually one person monopolizing the process. There are many types of groups and their usage depends on therapy goals. I find several different types of group therapy beneficial to the recovering alcoholic and his family depending on their stage of recovery. A sampling of the groups offered within my practice in support of this effort are described briefly within the following paragraphs.

Phase One Group: A basic group for the early stage recovering alcoholic in which all members have less than two months of sobriety. Within this group, the focus is on feelings and the expression of them through both physical and verbal outlets. Group members are expected to participate in an active way. Pillows and sponge rubber clubs are utilized in order to help the individual release anger and other pent-up emotions, if necessary.

All too often, however, inexperienced therapists will concentrate on *anger therapy* in which the expression of anger is the end goal. This is wrong. Any anger that has been dwelling within the individual for longer than thirty seconds is **contaminated** anger (see glossary and appendix—Mt. St. Helen's Syndrome). This type of anger always has an underlying component to it. It must be remembered that the alcoholic has denied feelings for quite some time. Feelings of shame, guilt, sadness, hurt, and anger have been suppressed again and again. It is ridiculous to expect only anger to come of all that. In fact, as indicated in the Mt. St. Helen's Syndrome concept, the anger seen within group is pseudo (false) anger. It is a contamination of some other feeling or combination of feelings.

Therefore, I utilize the energy garnered from the pseudo anger and trace it to its source. Often as not, hurt is the prime motivator underlying anger within the alcoholic. Repeatedly, I have witnessed prolonged expressions of grief, i.e., crying and verbalization of hurt, following outbursts of pseudo anger. The therapist must pursue the emotional outbursts and "take it to its source." My favorite saying regarding this matter is, "Show me an angry person who has not been immediately stimulated to anger, and I'll show you a person who hurts."

The degree of hurt and time of not dealing with the hurt is directly proportional to the intensity of displayed anger. In other words, the level of pseudo anger is a good indicator of how long the person has lived with his or her hurt. Of course, no actual physical abuse is permitted. A group member might hit his fist into the pillow, for example, or hit the floor with a sponge rubber club, but no one is ever permitted to strike another group member with or without props. I am very demanding within this group and allow no one to be a *bar stool eavesdropper, window peeper* or a *bar-flower*. They must actively participate.

Group Psychodrama: This form of therapy is usually reserved for group members with at least one month sobriety. The active group member who wants to work on utilizing this technique becomes the "star" of a play in which other group members perform supporting roles. The play is based on a segment of the star's own life history in which we re-enact one or more episodes cut from it. Usually involving the star's family, he or she will choose the time, place, and incident. It might, for example, be an incident that took place at dinner table when the star was ten years old.

The stage is set according to star's memory. Present were parents, sister, and a childhood friend. The incident might be that father belittled star in front of a friend in such a way that star's feelings were hurt. The feeling was suppressed because the star felt no freedom to express feelings outright to father or anyone else. Over the years, pseudo anger developed resulting from the suppression. Through psychodrama, we allow the group member (star) to work through this incident and take care of old business. Even though it is twenty years later, the healing process occurs pretty much the same as it would have at the time of the incident if star had taken corrective action then.

As you might think, the corrective action in this case would not have been to confront the father through anger. A more therapeutic outcome would be realized if John were able to get in touch with the real feelings relative to the accidental "put down" by his father. Of course, John, the star, needs to relive the emotion and, with group assistance, express the hurt. John's statement to his father might have been, "Dad, when you speak to me that way, it hurts my feelings and embarrasses me in front of my friend." In the group psychodrama scene, John would be encouraged by the audience (group members not having a role in the play) to "Take care of your feelings, John," or "That a way, John. Get your feelings out." That's it. No manipulation in hopes of an apology from Dad, but just an expression of John's feelings. Simple. More of this concept is presented during the discussion of the Mt. St. Helen's Syndrome theory within this chapter.

Psychodrama is used less formally and without so much structure in a group therapy technique that we call **role play**. Utilizing role play, the group leader either chooses a group member to play a single role or he, the leader, may elect to do so. This quick psychodrama technique requires little or no rehearsing and is more spontaneous than when using classic psychodrama. A group member, for example, might be having difficulties with her boss and can't seem to confront her with the problem. Another group member who more closely resembles the boss might be asked to accept that role and a *mini* psychodrama is enacted.

The troubled group member is encouraged to ventilate her feelings and to possibly develop strategy by which she can confront the boss and eliminate the problem. The role play technique is quite useful within this group because of the clients' outpatient status.

They are working and carrying on their normal daily activities while attending therapy in the evenings or some other convenient time. The client needs to have immediate outlets for his frustrations as they occur. If not, he may resort to old methods of dealing with them which, of course, was drinking. I encourage the use of psychodrama techniques to deal with these daily problems because of its effectiveness and the many variations of role playing available.

Family Group: Very simply, this group consists of one or more families. The total number within this group, as in all other groups, should not exceed eleven. Each and every family member has equal space and freedom in the group. Issues relative to recovery are worked through utilizing the EPA theory of recovery as well as other concepts. This group is somewhat less structured than groups mentioned thus far and is used throughout the treatment program.

Ex-Spouse Group: This is one of my favorite groups, relegated to the ex-spouses of alcoholics or ex-partners of long term relationships with one. We identify and work on cleaning up psychological and emotional debris remaining from the sick marriage or relationship. All long term relationships of a "living together" quality are treated as if legally married. As a matter of interest, I use divorce adjustment counseling with all clients of a terminated, living together relationship whether married or not. It never ceases to surprise me at the residual guilt, self-blaming, and lowered self-esteem ex-spouses have long after the alcoholic spouse is gone.

Phase Three Group: This is a unique group relegated to the recovering alcoholic who is reintegrating into society. Psychodrama and role play is very prevalent within this group as we set up scenarios in which each member is expected to participate. The primary goal of this group is to help identify Experiential Primal Anxiety (EPA) sources within each group member and work toward its reduction. Techniques used include, but are not limited to, dancing, meeting at restaurants to enjoy dinner together, and acting out various social events. Any group member may request interaction in which he or she needs to confront EPA. Within reason, the phase three group would provide as much anxiety stimulating interaction for the member as possible.

Relapse Group: Specifically for the alcoholic in all phases of recovery, this group focuses on those who have suffered relapse, or think they might. Participation of group members is structured in an effort to prevent the feared relapse or to reestablish recovery after having experienced relapse. Concepts relative to relapse are discussed along with educational presentations on the subject and an occasional guest group member.

We now return to our imaginary client, John. He is placed in a group with other recovering alcoholics. Within this group, John's views on his ability to control alcohol intake, his insistence on certain reasons for his drinking, and, in general, his entire denial system are challenged. This time, however, the challenge and confrontation are not coming from a counselor necessarily, but from people just like John. His attitude and beliefs waver as others who are nothing more than acquaintances challenge his views. They do this while sharing with him and other group members how they, too, used to think just like John. Through this process, his denial system begins to lose its thick protective armor. A small chink here, a dent there, and pretty soon a rupture or hole in the armor appears. John is making progress.

Progress is painful for John and others recovering from alcoholism. There is a reluctance to relinquish a substance that has provided so much. For years, alcohol has been John's best friend, his lover, his doctor, his counselor and worst of all, his method of coping with society's pressures. John can't remember the last time he danced without being fortified with alcohol or the last time he got together with friends, relatives or business acquaintances without drinking. It has been years since John made love to his wife on a prolonged regular basis without alcohol being present as a significant factor. Invariably, he has found some reason to celebrate with alcohol prior to his love making.

Furthermore, on those weekend fishing or business trips, alcohol was all John needed. Who needs friends when you have booze? Who wants to give up this relationship? Who wants to pour out the substance that steadied the shaking hand and the quivering knees so another work day could be faced?_Of course, John's denial system fights hard to retain alcohol in a positive light. While blinding him to reality, it was the provider of all the above qualities. John's denial system continues to drop and his reality becomes real as group and individual therapy progresses, along with continuing education.

John is now ready for phase two. Although the alcohol is physically out of his system (detox), and he hasn't drank for a month,

John is far from being well. He is moody, short tempered, rigid, very critical and, in short, miserable. He is experiencing what is referred to within the field of alcoholism counseling as a *dry drunk*. I, personally, do not use this term both because it is so difficult for the recovering person to understand plus it does not adequately describe him in this phase of recovery. Actually, he is **unstable** (see glossary).

Basically, any implication that the alcoholic is still drunk, dry or otherwise, will cause negative consequences. He immediately rejects such labeling and uses a great deal of mental energy to fight the counselor on this point. He will insist that he is sober, yielding only after very lengthy argument and educational effort to the contrary. Even when the alcoholic reluctantly admits, "I am a dry drunk," he invariably does not totally understand or agree with this concept. He will often say, "If I am a dry drunk, I might as well be a wet one."

This is all wasted time and energy, which would be better spent on other recovery issues. That is not to say John isn't exhibiting drunk behavior, because he is. The irritability and miserableness is there all right. It also influences negatively everyone who interacts with John much the same as it was when he drank. Expressions of, "He was easier to get along with in many respects when he was drinking," is typically heard from significant others in phase two. John's behavior is not only common, but also predictable at this stage of his recovery.

John has made a monumental decision in giving up his "crutch" and primary coping method. Wouldn't you be bitter, sad and irritable if all that were taken away? In addition to John's psychological irritability resulting from the aforementioned, there is a definite physical complication. His nerves are waking up after being anesthetized by the chemical. His tolerance level of the children's noise and of work frustrations is much lower than when he was "fortified" by alcohol. This feeling might be compared to the peace and tranquility of being alone in a boat on a lake. You can see people or cars on a distant shore, but not hear them. All of a sudden, you are put right in the middle of a downtown traffic jam during rush hour. Wouldn't that be traumatic?

Yes, John has reason to be miserable. In phase two, John is an unstable recovering alcoholic. He is sick, sad, sober and sorry. John is also miserable, bitter and resentful. All this is present, though diminishing, throughout phase two of John's recovery process. This phase can take days, weeks or months depending on three factors:

1) John's motivation, 2) counselor's knowledge and therapy ability, and 3) the quality and quantity of education John receives.

I view educational sessions with the recovering alcoholic and his significant others as having an equal role in the recovery process along with therapy. In fact, therapy is education and education is therapy. Each have different settings and the counselor's role might change somewhat. In the final analysis, however, there is but one goal; help the client override his subconscious resistance to recovery. This is accomplished by breaking down the defensive wall and penetrating his denial system.

Technically, one might label the work done in breaking through John's defensive wall as therapy or counseling. We could also say the techniques described herein such as group, family and individual therapy are used to accomplish that goal. On the other hand, one might view the process geared toward penetrating his denial system as educational.

There are those who will argue that denial and defense are the same or, more accurately, that denial is a form of defense. In psychological terminology, they would be correct. I find it to be much more helpful to John and myself to separate these two terms while using a different setting for each and labeling them differently. It has been my experience in observing the client that he relaxes a little more in an educational setting. It could be that he feels like a student again who has to do nothing else but listen. Of course, if the therapist is also doing the education, a golden opportunity is present to do what I refer to as "incidental therapy". I will not dwell on this, but feel certain that the reader, and especially other professionals, will understand.

As John and his family progress in the recovery process, I add more information while re-hashing the old. You see, the denial system greatly impairs John's ability to process at the conscious level information that would confirm alcoholism. Therefore, we must do this, at the beginning, in small increments and by constant repetition. It might help to understand this concept by referring once again to my own recovery. You might recall the statement made in the prologue about not being aware of the damage done to my body and mind by alcohol until I awoke in a mental health facility in 1974. You might also recall that my recovery process started in 1968 and that by 1974, I had been in four mental institutions due to my alcoholism.

Surely, basic alcohol information must have been provided before 1974, even though my alcoholism had not been addressed directly.

Although treatment of the disease was not nearly as sophisticated as it is today, basic alcoholism information must have been made available. My subconscious denial system may have blocked that information from my conscious awareness. Obviously, it escaped my consciousness, possibly due to presentation methods. This, in turn, allowed my denial system to convert it to a distortion of what was said in order to support my continued drinking. Of course, nothing processed to my consciousness.

The question immediately arises as to why did my subconscious allow me to hear the information correctly in 1974? The answer to that question is the essence of therapy. Was it because of repetition? Had I been inundated with the information until it finally registered? Did the complex mechanism of the brain finally decide that the entire organism was being destroyed by alcohol? If so, did it take corrective action by allowing me to become consciously aware of the need to stop drinking? I do not know. I do believe, however, that a continual repetition of anti-drinking information and different methods of getting this same information across to the alcoholic is necessary, especially in the early stages of recovery.

Simplicity works in most cases, but occasionally, more complicated approaches work better. With some alcoholics, one must use a completely experiential or demonstrational approach. With others, a more intellectual approach works better. Having little to do with the alcoholic's education or level of sophistication, the approach seems to be more a measure of whether he or she is a doer or a thinker. I use both approaches to get a feel of "what's getting through" and then concentrate more heavily accordingly. Sometimes, it is necessary to go back and forth with both approaches.

At any rate, my experience has been that new information must be given in small doses. Further, it must be assumed that all information is not received by the alcoholic. This assumption prevails until he shows some clear indication of reception and understanding. We need to watch for signs that he is not just repeating what was said to him. We also need to be aware that the alcoholic is not just complying with some type of activity. There must be a clear statement in his own words or actions representing complete awareness. This has to come from his thinking level. Also, he must show expression at the emotional level. Finally, he must be motivated to apply concepts at the social level. That, my friend, is a tall order, but when these three things happen, John is ready to advance into another phase of treatment.

The counselor can then proceed to new material without re-hashing the previous concepts quite so much. When this happens, there is a subtle, ever so slight, change that the therapist, who is in tune to the client, will perceive. Sometimes, however, the change is so dramatic that anyone can perceive it. To help in this area, I always ask the recovering person's spouse and significant others to share every observation they might have.

Without prompting the spouse, I listen for statements such as, "John holds me just a little longer than he used to when we caress." They might say, "There is something different about John's interaction with the children. He really seems to care about what they are saying to him and he to them." These little clues will help the counselor to continue his on-going assessment of John's recovery progress. Of course, this helps to determine when he is ready for another phase of treatment. Only when the time is right can the counselor proceed to new material. Until then we continue to re-hash the old even to the point of insulting his intelligence. In my estimation, it is better to bore the client than assume that he understands. The process of completing this second phase of recovery can take days, weeks, or months and, unfortunately, for some it never happens.

We will assume that John is hearing the information presented in education and is responding well to therapy. Additionally, he is assimilating this into both his mental and emotional frame of reference and reacting accordingly. Also, the rigidity, frustration, irritability and overall level of being miserable are either gone or have significantly diminished. Remember, these were present at high levels when he first entered phase two. He and his family are then ready for a major step in their recovery process.

This step calls for the implementation of the social component of my Experiential Primal Anxiety (EPA) therapy. This therapy is applied only after John has a good grasp on all previous concepts. Also, he must be actively participating in his own recovery and show motivation toward re-integration into society. Yes, re-integration is necessary even though John is being treated on an outpatient basis and is not physically removed from society. If he were being treated inpatient, then this would begin his discharge phase and constitute after care. In every treatment approach, there is a definite need for re-socialization.

In the chapter on causation, you will recall the discussion about my EPA theory and the developmental gap. It was stated therein that EPA (anxiety) is inherent at various levels in all experiences. Persons who choose to use alcohol or any means to avoid EPA will not advance in growth socially for that experience. You will also recall that a natural reduction of EPA occurs if one confronts the anxiety-provoking social situation or experience. Furthermore, this confrontation must be without using alcohol or any other type of drug to artificially lower the anxiety. In addition, continued confrontation with the experience will cause one to grow socially and mature naturally relative to the social event (dancing). He would then experience diminished levels of EPA, when confronted with future dancing experiences. Finally, no developmental gap would occur and the individual would be socially mature for the event.

Likewise, it was stated that avoidance, not confronting the experience head on, was possible through three methods. One was through actually leaving the situation by physical avoidance. The second method of avoidance was through mental means, which will not be discussed within this book. The third was by alcohol or some other drug. It is easily understandable that one will not grow, learn, or develop socially if he physically avoids the experience. How can one learn, for example, what it is like to dance unless he does so?

A little more difficult to understand is that a similar lack of growth and development will result if one uses alcohol to reduce the anxiety. Growth will not be experienced even though one physically continues the experience. In other words, a developmental gap occurs for that event. This in turn will cause a reoccurrence of the EPA at a socially crippling level each and every time one is confronted with the avoided experience. If this concept seems unclear to you, please read again the section discussing my EPA theory of alcoholism causation.

As John enters phase three of his recovery process, it is time to evaluate the extent of his developmental gap. Actually, I've been keeping an ongoing record throughout John's treatment. This was accomplished by logging what John had to say in individual, group and family therapy and watching his actions and reactions to people, places and events. Essentially, all of John's behavior while in treatment contributed to my perception of his social and mental age.

Every time John showed a reluctance to do certain simple, social functions or interactions, it was recorded. Notation was made when he sat next to a certain person during group therapy or avoided certain social niceties such as hugging. Also, special attention was given to John's history as related by his parents, wife and children, and all those within his *significant others* category. This information was correlated with John's own historical information and inconsistencies were noted. After that, John's mental and social base-line profile was further substantiated by using certain psychological testing.

If done prematurely, psychological testing of the alcoholic can be very misleading because of the dramatic effect that alcohol has on the mental processes and emotional system. This effect prevails long after the alcoholic ceases to drink and sometimes he or she may never regain full mental or emotional stability. The following information is provided as further evidence of the disturbed thinking that alcoholics experience. It is not meant to instruct the reader on usage of psychological testing or to necessarily explain the instrument under discussion.

The information referred to herein resulted from three years of testing a population of alcoholics within two different inpatient treatment facilities. There were two groups tested; those who had been sober less than six days and those more than six. All were tested after acute detoxification so none were acutely under the influence of alcohol or "drunk". Participants were asked to take the test under controlled conditions with standard instructions being communicated.

The Minnesota Multiphasic Personality Inventory (MMPI) was used. It is an instrument used to measure mental and emotional stability in many areas of the personality including, but not limited to, depression, social withdrawal, paranoia (intense suspiciousness of others' intentions and fear of encroachment from others), impulsivity (bull in a China shop tendency), schizophrenia (inaccurate perception of reality), hypochondriases (preoccupation with one's health and ulcer-type sickness), anxiety and mental energy (mind cannot remain on one subject for long). In measuring one's "normalcy", we observe peaks and valleys of the graph (see appendix). There are three dark lines with the upper-most one reflecting presence of the trait in a pathological **sick** direction, the middle line indicating absolute normal, and the bottom line reflecting a pathological absence of the trait being measured.

The results of my study presented herein leave little doubt that alcohol grossly affects one's mental processes. Observe, for example, how the peaks are dramatically reduced after just seven days of total abstinence. The peaks, of course, indicate pathology or confused thinking. Normal profiles find peaks within the two extreme dark lines with absolute normal being the dark center line. Notice how the group experiencing less than seven days without alcohol are peaked above the heavy line. This is the line representing the outer limits of normalcy. More importantly, these results reflect how the human mind continues to be influenced after cessation of drink.

Several inferences can be made from this study, one being that accurate psychological testing of the alcoholic is impossible prior to a prolonged period of complete and total abstinence. The question is often raised as to what is a safe period of time to wait prior to testing the recovering alcoholic. To be safe, I would recommend at least two months. Of course, there are many factors to consider prior to making this determination. One must consider, for example, the client's age, overall general physical and mental condition, time he or she has been an active alcoholic, and the extent of usage.

There is a test that I use in conjunction with my theory of alcoholism causation and treatment which was designed specifically to determine the developmental gap. Measuring one's self-perceived anxiety (see appendix), The **Subjective Anxiety Measurement Scale** (SAMS) contains ten scenarios or situations in which the individual is asked to mentally place himself. By responding to each scenario on a scale from one to seven with one being none and seven being unmanageable, the individual's EPA level is recorded. These scores are totalled to give an overall EPA profile.

One might be asked, for example, to imagine being involved in an initiation for lodge membership in which they are asked to sing the National Anthem on a street corner. The respondent would then indicate on the SAMS scale the degree of anxiety he or she might feel relative to that experience. He then replies accordingly for the remaining questions. The total scale numbers, when compiled, indicate the individual's degree of anxiety awareness. The primary use of the SAMS is to determine one's level of maturity. The individual showing high levels of anxiety relative to certain social interactions would be seen as immature socially depending on their age and experience. The SAMS, of course, is just one of many factors used to determine social immaturity which is synonymous with the developmental gap. The counselor's observation, as well as client, family, and significant others' reports have the most weight in making this determination.

Once John's developmental gap has been established, we begin working to close it. This is probably the single most important factor in recovery that treatment centers and private practitioners overlook. Evidently, they just do not understand what must be done after the drinking behavior ends. They seem to think John will fit right back into society now that drinking has stopped. On the contrary, he drank to escape from that society, components of which were anxiety provoking then and certainly will be again. What did John do when confronted with anxiety? He avoided it through drink. What will he do about it now? Probably the same, unless he learns and develops different coping strategies. We must help him confront the *Experiential Anxiety* head on this time. Of course, we have been doing that gradually through therapy and educational sessions, but now we concentrate our majority effort in the direction of re-integration.

John is not only encouraged to participate in social functions, but also scheduled to do so. If preparation is necessary prior to the event, he is so prepared. Say, for example, that John is planning to attend his high school reunion and dancing will be expected. Further, we realize that John can't dance too well and has only done so while under the influence of alcohol. Rather than suggest that John wear a fake cast to the dance or in any other way be a wall-flower, we ask John to take dance lessons. We also ask his wife to take lessons right along with John or, if she is a good dancer, teach him to dance. Gradually, we expose John to dancing, possibly relegating group time to this effort. In phase three groups, we really deviate from "normal" group procedures. As John gains confidence in dancing, his enthusiasm for attending the reunion should also be on the rise.

Similarly, other areas of John's social life are analyzed and levels of EPA relative to each are discussed. A simple task of going to a movie downtown might create a five or seven level of EPA. For years, John has either gone to a drive-in movie with a cooler of beer and/or a pint of whiskey in the car or watched movies on television. He usually used the excuse that movies were too expensive, too crowded, or that he couldn't sit still, smoke, or relax. His real reason for not going, of course, was that he could not take his alcohol with him.

John will want to continue doing things in which he feels comfortable, such as watching television, but we won't allow it. Recovery is an active and social process and in order to be a stable alcoholic, one must be able to get into the thick of things. Not that he must do all of these things, but he must be able to. Therefore, we find what John doesn't like to do socially. This indicates an area needing work, so we work in that direction.

I remember a client that we virtually had to push into a dance group and now he is dancing as an avocation. His was pretty much the same old story. He danced while under the influence but denied even having the desire to do so when sober. My own personal recovery utilized this approach. I did take dance lessons and, though not a Fred Astaire, can cut a pretty good figure on the dance floor and really enjoy myself within that capacity.

As phase three continues, John's family, civic, and social involvement improves. He becomes an active part of the school system. Although complaining for years about "the lousy school system" and never once visiting the school, he will become active in PTA or fund raising, assist in coaching, or give class presentations. More importantly, he will be a part of his children's world more so than ever before.

Within this effort, as in all social recovery, the key is to approach the least desirable and most avoided responsibilities. After practice, those things previously avoided might become the most attractive once the EPA is reduced sufficiently to allow participation. For the first time, John might actually meet his neighbors. John probably doesn't know who the next door neighbor is. Also, through the haze of alcohol, he either suspects ill feelings, or harbors ill feelings toward him. At any rate, John needs to become more community oriented.

The progression of phase three is witnessed by the continued civic mindedness of John and his enthusiasm for social interaction. With social intercourse, the question always arises as to whether a recovering alcoholic should frequent parties where alcoholic beverages are served. To this I say, "absolutely not" while in phase one or two, but "yes" in phase three. My reasoning is that in phases one and two, the alcoholic is unstable. Unstable, remember, is **Unhappy, Nervous, Sick-Thinking, Alcohol Behavior Link Evident**. With such inner turmoil, one is just waiting for an excuse to get drunk. Unrehearsed social pressures would provide just such an excuse. If we add the availability of alcohol to the need for a drink, then you are in trouble. In fact, I require all my clients in phases one and two not to socialize where alcoholic beverage is a prominent factor. They are especially cautioned not to go to a bar in order to drink Pepsi *just to prove I can sit there, chew the fat with friends and not drink*. That is asking for trouble with a capital "T". A bar sells primarily one thing--alcohol.

In phase three, however, the alcoholic is closer to being stable which means **Sober Thinking, Alcohol Behavior Link Eliminated**. At this time, he is not looking for an excuse to drink and his behavior is not a result of subconscious process manipulation. It is time John stops allowing alcohol to control his life. For years, John has been directly under its control. Now that stability is nigh, he wants to relinquish all behavior control that alcohol has on him, even indirect control.

Further explanation of indirect control might be helpful. Suppose John chooses to avoid all functions where alcohol is served for the rest of his sober life. Suppose also that John is invited to a social function that his entire family would like to attend. John says no because there will be alcohol available as a social gesture. Further, John decides not to attend his own retirement party for the same reason even though his best friends and co-workers are there to honor him. Who is controlling what in this situation? Better yet, what is controlling whom? You guessed it. John is definitely being controlled indirectly by alcohol in the situations presented.

It is wise to be cautious, however; if alcohol becomes too attractive or people become obnoxious, don't hesitate to leave a party. Also, one must be absolutely sure he is on solid ground prior to going where alcohol is served. A good rule of thumb is if in doubt, forget the party and go to an AA meeting instead. A good counselor can always help by giving you constructive feedback. Finally, if you find yourself frequenting parties, etc., where you know alcohol is a prominent factor, it is time to really analyze your motivation. It could be you are leading up to a relapse. It is necessary to emphasize here that phase three recovery is an on-going life time effort. It is one in which we continually improve ourselves and learn. We enjoy life to its fullest and do not contaminate it with any type of mood altering chemical. After a while, alcohol seems so remote that we begin to lose sight of our alcoholism. That, too, is dangerous. Although not dwelling on my alcoholism, the thought that I am only one drink away from a drunk is always a mindful factor. This thought helps prevent relapse which is the next topic.

Relapse is feared by all recovering alcoholics whether in phase one, two or three. It is defined as the unwanted and unplanned return to a previous phase of recovery. The key words are *unplanned* and *unwanted*. The alcoholic who consciously plans to get drunk and claims a relapse is just lying. Relapse is a phenomenon that, in my estimation, is never consciously planned, but is a product of the subconscious (see appendix).

The lay person has a great deal of difficulty understanding this aspect of recovery. Probably the best example I can give to explain how relapse works is by again referring to my own recovery. A relapse occurred for me in March of 1975 because I failed to see it coming six months previously. In November of 1974, I had experienced nine months of sobriety, was in my second quarter of college, was in love and was doing great. The thought began to plague me that, "Maybe I am not an alcoholic. Maybe all that drinking was because of the military. Maybe it was because of the terrible readjustment to society after being booted from the military. Maybe it was because of the lousy jobs." The clincher was, "Because nobody really understood me." My thinking continued like that for a while until one day a "brilliant" idea of testing myself came to mind. It occurred to me that no alcoholic could drink just one bottle of beer and stop. A decision was made to try one bottle of beer a day while watching the daily six o'clock news. My strategy was to try this for a month. A definite plan was made to stop immediately if one bottle within any twenty-four hour period was exceeded.

It is almost comical to think of such a thing at this time, but ten years ago, it sounded absolutely brilliant. The reader must realize I was dead serious. If present, deceivement was definitely a subconscious to conscious process. The experiment was successfully conducted for one whole month until mid-December when a step closer to relapse took place. Further brilliant thinking reasoned that a six pack of beer within one week was the same if taken one per night (I didn't drink one on Sunday) or all at the same time. Moreover, I decided that since my experiment was so successful thus far, why not advance to another plateau?

My strategy was to save all those nightly beers for Saturday night and drink them at one sitting while watching Saturday Night Live. Brilliant! Just to be sure, however, I extended the one beer per day deadline for another month without a hitch. In January, 1975, plan two went into operation and for almost two months, it worked. In fact, because these two experiments proved successful and it was proven that *controlled* drinking was possible, my fate was sealed. Relapse was inevitable; it was just a matter of time.

It happened on the last day of the winter quarter. About four or five of us were sitting in the Student Union when a fellow student came in with a bottle of whiskey and passed it around. When it came my turn, there was a moment's hesitation. Hadn't the experiment shown me to have control over alcohol? I took a big drink in answer to my silent question and took another each time the bottle came around. By the time my ride came, I was drunk.

The conscious mind realized too late that any control it had over alcohol was a myth. Once again, the subconscious had played a trick and the conscious foolishly believed it. We stopped at the liquor store on the way home and bought a fifth. Two fifths were bought the next day since it was Saturday and, at that time, the sale

of whiskey was illegal on Sunday in Ohio. To make a long story
short, my drunk lasted for ten days. During that time, I experienced
blackouts and while in them exhibited very bizarre behavior. It was
the type of behavior which would have caused me to be immediately
expelled. Fortunately for me, Dr. Gerald O'Brien, who was my student advisor and department head, recognized it as alcoholic behavior and treated me accordingly. As a result of his intervention, in
conjunction with Dr. Larry Haverkos, a decision was made to allow
my college career to continue. Had it not been for that decision, this
book would not have been written.

Dr. O'Brien took quick and effective action which, essentially,
caused me to stop and reevaluate myself. He gave me a choice to
stay on the sidewalk or go back to the gutter. That was on Monday,
March 17, 1975. My last drink was taken that day just prior to
talking with Dr. O'Brien. Incidentally, the remainder of the fifth of
whiskey with only the one drink missing (a big one) was poured
down the drain after that talk. Spring quarter classes were due to
start Wednesday. That left one day to get myself together from a ten
day drunk and back into class. The body made it on schedule, but
my mind didn't clear up for almost two weeks. Mind and body got
together by mid-term, however, and the rest is history.

To think of how disasterous it could have been makes me shud-
der. It would have been all because of my stupid and hardheaded
reluctance to admit that alcohol had beat me. Look at how my mind
engineered that relapse. It took almost six months for my subconscious processes to get me drunk, but there I was. In refering to my
sobriety experiment, one might say that the operation was a success,
but the patient died. That's the way it is when one plays the alcohol
game. There are no winners, but the subconscious doesn't seem to
care.

While writing this, my subconscious just sent a message to the
conscious saying, "What if you had only drank beer? It was whiskey
that did you in." If not for my stable condition, this thought might
be worth analyzing. But I am a stable recovering alcoholic now and
know better. It was just a matter of time from the first beer in
November years ago until that terrible relapse and total loss of
control. The same thing would happen today. When these messages
are received now, I can act to short circuit the relapse process.

The recovering alcoholic must be trained to recognize when he is
in a relapse posture. This is extremely difficult because of the influence put upon the conscious mind by the subconscious processes. It
is the subconscious once again telling us to drink and setting *traps*

to influence our conscious mind to do so. You see, only the conscious mind can make decisions to act, but the subconscious provides the material by which to decide. The recovering alcoholic, therefore, must establish a validating system whereby his thoughts are analyzed. One's counselor is probably the best qualified to do this, but the spouse or a close friend is also helpful. Your AA sponsor (see glossary) should be utilized whenever possible. In fact, the more people you know that can give honest and accurate feedback, the better.

Simply asking these trusted persons from time to time what their thoughts are about your ideas and behavior might be interesting. You might inquire, for example, what they think about your plans to go on a weekend fishing trip with old buddies. They might point out that Tom and Jerry are heavy drinkers and always take plenty of booze with them on those trips. They might also bring to your attention how angry and frustrated you become when your catch is zero. Further, it might be exposed that your favorite relaxation after a day's fishing was to sit around the campfire swapping stories and really "mellowing out" on beer and whiskey. Finally, they might remind you that you always returned drunker than any of the others. This information could then be processed within the conscious and acted on accordingly.

Another short circuiting mechanism my clients prepare is a relapse warning guide (see appendix). In this, each individual is asked to outline what he would see as an early indication of relapse. He might include stopping at a bar "just to drink a Pepsi" on his list. If he should then have a notion to do such a thing, he has an immediate conscious alarm available that he is heading for relapse and, therefore, can short circuit such behavior. This relapse warning guide is carried in the wallet and when coupled with a good sobriety plan, can be very effective in relapse prevention.

Since one can never be too safe, further protection might be advisable. You might ask trusted friends and relatives to let you know if they see any dramatic changes in your frustration level, or if you are picking arguments. Ask them to report on any dramatic changes at all, especially, work habits or socialization conduct. Ask your spouse to be particularly keen on this. Request the entire family to give you feedback concerning your overall personality and to be especially keen on how you relate to them emotionally relative to kindness, warmth and love. The person ripe for relapse will transmit signals rarely perceived by the recovering person, himself. Therefore, the recovering alcoholic must be receptive to feedback and actually solicit this kind of help. Of course, Alcoholics Anonymous (AA), when used correctly, can be one of the most effective relapse preventions available.

Relapse can be helpful, if you truly have one and not a *lying drunk*. Remember, this is simply where the alcoholic plans a drunk outright and then pretends to have relapsed. The recovering alcoholic can benefit from his relapse, if he learns how his subconscious really works, or if he comes to fully accept his powerlessness over the chemical. Clearly, I learned of my complete and total powerlessness over alcohol as a result of my relapse. Relapse does happen and must not be viewed as the end, but rather as the beginning of another string of one day at a times. This is important! Many alcoholics will despair after relapse and possibly never sober up again. That is so unnecessary and damaging. Learn from it. Add to your relapse prevention by including events that led up to it this time and avoid such behavior next time.

Before ending this section of the chapter, I need to express concern and caution about some of the statements made within it. The recovering alcoholic might misconstrue what was presented and because of the subconscious processes and denial system, will probably do just that. One thing I wish to state emphatically is that the total responsibility of the recovering alcoholic to maintain his sobriety rests with him, the alcoholic. No way is it the responsibility of the feedback network suggested herein. In other words, getting drunk because your spouse didn't recognize that your behavior was headed in that direction does not make it his or her fault. It is your sobriety and only you are the final protector of it.

I would like to remind the reader how important it is to get proper treatment for the disease of alcoholism. My own recovery was delayed because of misdiagnosis and improper treatment. Ask for credentials and investigate the competency of your counselor by talking with his colleagues. Talk to former clients if possible and check with the professional organizations to which he or she is affiliated. Once again, treat this relationship with equal concern as you would with choosing a brain surgeon. In a certain sense, that is what you are doing.

We evidenced a client coming into treatment angry for many reasons, but primarily because of the loss of alcohol. Introduced was a three phase treatment program with its many components comprising each phase. Moreover, an imaginary client named John Smith and his family were followed through the recovery process using my theory of treatment.

Lastly, a section on relapse was presented in which it was explained that true relapse is a subconscious process frequently starting weeks or months prior to the actual relapse. A strong statement was made that continued sobriety in the final analysis is the responsibility of the recovering alcoholic. Finally, the recovering alcoholic was reminded that relapse can be a positive experience if he comes to realize and accept his powerlessness over alcohol. If he truly wants to reach such a decision, it is certainly possible. A statement from Schopenhauer, an eighteenth century philosopher, might just be correct. He said, "We do not want a thing because we have found reasons for it, we find reasons for it because we want it."

CHAPTER FOUR

FAMILY TREATMENT

The need to treat each and every member of an alcoholic's family was alluded to in the previous chapter. We will now take an in depth look at why it is necessary to do this. As in the previous chapter, we will use an imaginary family, John and the Smiths, for illustration and clarification purposes. It will be shown how John's sickness contaminates the entire Smith family and inundates their lives. Paradoxically, the family members become John's primary support mechanism which, in turn, makes it possible for him to continue drinking. In addition, it will be shown how John structures his family in such a way that they lose their identity and assume roles dictated by him. As in most alcoholic phenomena, this process is neither conscious nor planned. It couldn't be done with better precision, however, than if it were planned and rehearsed daily.

Every alcoholic must have a support system or he will fall flat on his face and, eventually, land right in the gutter. Only then, of course, will many alcoholics come to the full realization of the negative consequences of their drinking. Until they do so, recovery is impossible. Therefore, the initial task of counseling is to help the alcoholic come to this realization as quickly and completely as possible. To do so, we must first convince those supporting him to let go. An alcoholic's support system is a circle of relatives, friends, and acquaintances who interact with his drinking behavior. Moreover, they do this in such a way that he is denied the full negative aspects of it. They do it out of love and caring, but primarily out of ignorance.

The number one supporters are his immediate family, parents, boss, close friends and relatives. Notice I use the word close, for John will not associate with anyone on a close relationship who does not support his drinking. If you want to know who John's supporters are, just ask him who his real close friends are and who he trusts more than anyone else in the world. His answer will be the names of those who support his drinking behavior. He will shy away from those who do not support his drinking. In my own drinking past, the person I had the most difficulty with was my older brother. He had no stomach for alcohol, nor those who used it, and was very verbal with his convictions. Therefore, I avoided him like the plague. We now have a close relationship.

Many professionals refer to this circle of supporters as an *enabling system*. I prefer to use *support system* for several reasons. First of all, I do not feel the term *enabling* adequately describes the process. John is not just being enabled to drink; he is being supported. He is supported by those who would "loan" him money or keep him on the job when he misses work or doesn't perform adequately. He is supported by those who listen to his tales of woe and don't confront his alcoholism behavior. He is supported when given a place to live without paying room and board. This applies to teenagers or young men still living with parents. It also applies to spouses or relatives or anyone being *kept* because they drink up their money. This activity and any similar type of "help" for the alcoholic is not enabling but outright supporting.

I believe the term *enabling* infers that too much responsibility is relegated to a second party for John's drinking. An alcoholic's entire sick thoughts are already rife with a list of people and things to blame for his drinking and certainly needs no more. Finally, this entire concept is a difficult one for most family members to understand and accept. Any vague or incorrect terminology only adds to the confusion and creates more resistance within the family member. They do understand and accept this concept more readily when shown how they are *supporting* drunken behavior. On the other hand, family members have difficulty understanding or accepting that they are *enabling* John to drink. In my experience, changing the wording has helped immensely to get this concept across.

Although the term "enabling" has merit among professionals in describing the alcoholic's support system, it is far too cumbersome and inadequate a description of the phenomenon to be fully understood by the layman. The alcoholic, especially, misinterprets its meaning and, as explained earlier, uses it as another *blaming* tool. Support system, therefore, is used within this book to describe the phenomenon. But what exactly are we talking about? Although this concept has been alluded to in previous chapters, no complete definition has been given. As you will see, John's primary support system is usually his family, therefore, this chapter is the most appropriate one in which to discuss his support system in depth.

The best way to define an alcoholic's support system might be to describe its dynamics. John drinks too much and does something stupid at a party and his wife explains, "Well, you know how John is when he has a little too much to drink." Another example of these dynamics is when John is too sick the next day to go to work and Mrs. Smith calls and tells the boss that John has the flu. Another might be that John goes to jail for some drunken stupidity and mother bails him out. Also, a good example is that John comes home really drunk, falls asleep on the couch and vomits all over it. Mrs. Smith gets him to the bathroom, cleans him up, cleans up his mess and manages to get him in bed. An example of child support is when John comes home drunk and disrupts one of the children's birthday parties. The child explains that, "Daddy wasn't feeling well and hasn't been himself." Finally, John loses his job and the entire family agrees that it was too much pressure on him and he really wasn't understood or appreciated anyhow. We could continue with example after example. It is important that family members understand this concept because, like I said, they are the primary supporters.

Do you see how John is being deprived of realizing the full negative consequences of his drinking? In the first example, Mrs. Smith made excuses for John when he made a fool of himself at the party. It would have been better had she let him confront his foolishness. Also, she outright lied for him in the second example. The fourth example is classic. If she cleans up John's messes and John, himself, he is totally unaware of his drunken behavior. He awakens between two clean sheets with only a vague idea of being such a drunken bum the night before. Even the children support him. They, of course, do it out of embarrassment. The entire family is embarrassed for John. Further in this chapter, you will see how this excuse making and taking care of John causes the support system to gain strength.

As stated earlier, every alcoholic must have a support system or he will be incapable of continued drinking. As his alcoholism progresses, he loses an ability to cope with life and its complications. When this happens, he turns to his support system for "help" and, slowly but surely, turns all responsibility over to them. Unfortunately, he also gives up responsibility for his drinking as well. Throughout, the alcoholic appears to maintain a semblance of *control* over his life, but it is totally false.

Ironically, his family members probably enjoyed being in control of things for a while. The spouse, especially, feels very important in the capacity of *calling all the shots*, but as the disease progresses, he or she comes to the realization that it takes two to raise a family or make a marriage work. Through treatment, the alcoholic can again become part of that process and the family can get well together. Prior to discussing family treatment, per se, a brief review is in order to freshen our thoughts about alcoholism.

Remember that alcoholism is a disease that is primary, chronic, progressive and, if not treated, fatal. It is a disease that inundates the very essence of its victim. The mind, body, and soul all suffer from the devastating effects of alcohol. One's ability to think clearly and use logical reasoning becomes seriously impaired or non-existent. Emotions such as love, happiness, and even sadness give way to the disease as the alcoholic becomes unreal, uncaring and unfeeling.

The disease of alcoholism is somewhat like that of cancer in many respects. Alcoholism, for example, goes undetected until it reaches an advanced stage of progression. Also, like cancer, alcoholism has no respect for race, sex or position in life and attacks one and all alike with the same degree of disrespect and deteriorating quality. Furthermore, there is no known cause for alcoholism. Although many causative studies have been done, none can report a definitive finding as of this writing. Finally, like cancer, there is no cure for alcoholism. The symptoms can be treated, however, and its progressive nature interrupted if one adheres to a strict and total abstinence. The recovering alcoholic who re-learns to enjoy life must always be mindful that he is only a drink away from the living hell from whence he came. The recovering alcoholic should also be mindful that, unlike cancer, alcoholism has impacted upon all those with whom he is closely related, especially each member within his immediate family./

Until recently, however, very little has been done about this very serious consequence of alcoholism. It is becoming increasingly more apparent that alcoholism does as much damage, if not more, to the non-drinking family member than it does to the alcoholic himself. This damage is not just the classic financial loss, etc., that affects the family as a unit. It also renders a crippling influence upon the personality and essence of each family member. This damage is very similar to that experienced by the alcoholic even though the family member invariably is a tea-totaler.

It is with this understanding that more and more professionals within the field are recognizing alcoholism as a family disease. They are using approaches geared toward treating the non-alcoholic, but sick, family member. This phenomenon of family deformity resulting directly from alcoholism will be discussed throughout the remainder of this chapter. The discussion will focus specifically upon 1) causation, 2) effect, and 3) family systems approach to treatment.

The cause of family personality deformity is simply alcoholism. It is important to keep this one essential fact in mind while talking about consequences of alcoholism within the family. All too often, the alcoholic is blamed personally. In other words, it is assumed that he knowingly and purposefully causes the sickness within his family. This is a false assumption. While it is true that the alcoholic's sickness inundates the entire family, it is typically an unconscious process. In fact, the alcoholic rarely sees any problem relative to his family life until confronted with some precipitating crisis. This is usually a threatened divorce, runaway and/or chemically addicted child or some other family trauma. It must be remembered that the alcoholic's mental processes are impaired because of his own sickness. He is virtually seeing the world through a delusional system which, most assuredly, becomes his reality. These delusions are such that they enhance the alcoholic's perceived self-importance and justify his behavior. They also release him from responsibility which might interfere with his addiction.

The alcoholic will unconsciously structure his life, and the lives of those around him, in such a way as to confirm his delusions and deny or diminish reality. The degree to which he is successful in this endeavor will determine the degree of the family member's sickness. Conversely, it will also indicate the degree to which they become supporters of his disease. This then is the direct cause of personality deformity within the family. In other words, the alcoholic's illness causes the family member to suffer a form of fallout. This is an indirect result of alcoholism with very similar characteristics and devastating effects as those experienced by the alcoholic.

A full and complete understanding of this concept is necessary for the family to experience ultimate benefit from treatment. Its understanding is also important in order to work through strong negative feelings that are invariably directed toward the person instead of the disease. Further exploration of the early causative factors is in order with a detailed view of the alcoholic's progression from real to unreal. It is of particular interest for the family member to follow this progressive nature of the disease. This is because the family member experiences a similar personality deterioration as the alcoholic and at about the same rate. In other words, family deformity, like alcoholism, does not happen overnight, but is a long process sometimes taking years.

It will be recalled that the alcoholic was described as an unfeeling, uncaring and unreal entity. Although this is a true description of the advanced-stage alcoholic, it is certainly not true of the basic individual. Once again, it is important to separate the person from the illness. The alcoholic invariably was (and can be again) a loving, caring and real person. This real person, however, is slowly but methodically transformed into the sick and deformed person mentioned earlier. This becomes more observable as the progression of alcoholism takes its toll. The direction of progression is always a negative one and toward a more severe level and degree of sickness. The process is very similar across all social strata, is predictable and can be traced with a high degree of accuracy.

In the beginning stages of alcoholism, crises are relatively nonexistent and the alcoholic enjoys a rather harmless lifestyle of drinking. As the disease increases in severity, however, there is a continual increase in psychological pain resulting from the alcoholic's drinking behavior. Increasingly, he does things while under the influence which violate his value system and moral code. This is a system and code that everyone has unto himself and, when violated, causes psychological damage. This damage is typically in the form of lowered self-esteem and loss of the ability to experience self-love. The alcoholic, at this early stage, is not only aware of his behavior, but also often embarrassed and guilt-ridden. As you will see, the ability to experience these feelings won't last long.

He does not believe his own excuses or rationalizations at this time and only offers them to appease others to whom his drunken behavior has caused embarrassment. This is because the dishonesty and denial heard so often in conversations about alcoholism are not solidly in place during this early involvement. For now, at least, the alcoholic is aware of not only his feelings, his behavior and its family impact, but also his lost ability to control alcohol intake. He is also aware that drinking is no longer fun, but is satisfying some need which may or may not be within his awareness.

Continual drinking eventually causes the alcoholic's progression to more serious stages of alcoholism. Within these stages, classic behavioral changes take place. His behavior becomes increasingly more bizarre and atypical of his former self. Although the increased drinking and negative consequences thereof are apparent to others, the alcoholic fails to realize the problem. He begins to see problems inaccurately because of his delusional system. It is as if the alcoholic ceases to struggle with feelings associated with his negative actions. It seems that the final building block of a defensive wall goes into place at this time. This wall is now thick enough to insulate the real individual from harsh reality and allow the sick alcoholic to believe his own delusions. Both the dishonesty and denial mentioned earlier are now present. The alcoholic believes his own rationalizations and, therefore, is dishonest unto himself. A further explanation of this defensive wall concept will be helpful at this time (see appendix).

Seeking to diminish emotional and psychological pain resulting from his drinking, the alcoholic employs rationalizations. Very simply, this means he makes excuses. He also experiences delusions which means he sees himself completely different from reality. When this ceases to work, he simply drinks to cover the feelings and thoughts of shame, guilt, sadness, anger and fear. In other words, the alcoholic reaches a point of complete feeling denial. He does not want to confront any type of emotional stimuli which might bring negative attention to his drinking. Remember, this is self-denial of realistic feelings and emotions. It works in a very methodical progression from emotional pain to total denial through the alcohol.

Another example of this type of denial might be helpful. The alcoholic may do something stupid at a party, but doesn't remember doing it because he was in a blackout at the time (see glossary). When told the next day of his shameful behavior, the alcoholic does not allow himself the emotional turmoil associated with his behavior. Instead, he drinks to cover it up. There might have been shame, guilt and fear at a very high intensity, but a few shots of whiskey will take care of it.

Suppressing emotions like this over a prolonged period of time causes a very definite and dramatic consequence. Built around the alcoholic's real feelings, an imaginary wall goes into place. It serves to shield the alcoholic from not only other people, but also himself (see appendix). He then substitutes *phony* behavior which gives the appearance of being okay. Remember the section on the defensive wall in chapter three? John puts on a good show, but underneath he is falling apart. (See appendix)

What about the family members? How do they deal with their emotional and psychological pain? You guessed it. They, too, form defensive walls. This is done primarily as a result of living with a sick person. In any type of psychological and emotional illness (especially alcoholism), a fallout mechanism is present. Consequently, all within range will suffer. Association breeds similarity is very definite. If the well person does not get sick, then the sick person will get well, just through association.

Behavioral symptoms of the alcoholic throughout this process are many and varied. They can range from a passive aggressiveness during which the alcoholic is relatively quiet, yet cynically obtuse, to being openly aggressive. Within this latter state, he will threaten and might even do physical harm to himself or others. Furthermore, his moods will often change for no apparent reason. He can, for example, be extremely charming and then just as obnoxious all within the same setting. Moreover, the alcoholic will invariably exhibit a superior attitude and demean others whenever possible. This attitude seems to say, "Attack is the best defense".

Finally, the alcoholic's behavior, attitude and opinions are extremely rigid. They will be maintained without change even when confronted with the most convincing evidence to the contrary. This, of course, will create a most intense atmosphere in which to live. The alcoholic, nevertheless, methodically constructs such an atmosphere within his home. This, of course, is based on his sick thinking which is constructed from an unreal, delusional system. He then very rigidly preserves this position because he sees it as real.

As a result, the family members are confronted almost daily with a deplorable home life. In addition, they are forced to interact with such an unpredictable and confused person. How does the family member live within such an atmosphere? It is most difficult indeed. This is especially true when the alcoholic is often seen as an authority figure within the family structure. It is virtually impossible to live within such an atmosphere without also developing a sickness. In fact, many family members often become more sick than the alcoholic so described. This concept is discussed further within the following paragraphs. First, we need a little more information about family dynamics.

Because the family is a system, nothing occurs in isolation within it. Every member of a family experiences similar adjustments to everything. If a death or birth occurs within the family, all react accordingly. A graduation, promotion or wedding is reason for family adjustment. The family system is also affected throughout by any individual problems, especially alcoholism. Just like the alcoholic, each family member will exhibit certain symptoms of the illness. These symptoms will reflect the family member's own particular ability to conform to the alcoholic's delusion-based family system.

Each and every family member will find a place within that system through an unconscious process of seeking the area of least psychological pain. Moreover, each family member will know when they have reached a posture of least pain. This will be indicated by not only an absence of pain, but also the reward received from the alcoholic. The reward might be simply a relaxing of verbal abuse by the alcoholic or some material gift. Rewards can take many forms and they always reflect family member conformity. This is the sickness of which we are speaking.

As conformity is accomplished, the effects of alcoholism on the family as a unit and individually are dramatic. Each family member, for example, will adopt some method of coping within the family structure at a minimal level of physical, emotional and psychological pain. The absence of this pain usually means a compliance with the alcoholic's position and acceptance of his delusional system over that of reality. In order to adhere to such demands, each family member develops a defensive wall similar to that of the alcoholic's wall which, essentially, shields the member from emotional pain.

In addition to this defensive wall, each family member can be recognized by certain behavioral characteristics in keeping with expectations of the alcoholic. Essentially, each and every family member will develop role behavior and, in essence, become an actor on life's stage with the alcoholic being director. There are two types of roles that are developed within the alcoholic family. They are **alter-ego projected roles**, or simply, **ego roles** and **defensive roles**. The process just described within the last few paragraphs contributes to the development of defensive type roles. This is done almost entirely at the subconscious level as the family members seek to avoid psychological or physical pain.

Alter-ego roles, on the other hand, are developed at a higher level of consciousness and are a projection of John's alter-ego (see glossary). This is what he wants to be or how he sees himself. To a certain extent, all parents project their alter-ego onto their children. This is done at a more subtle level and normally is not as harmful to the child's growth and development as when done by the alcoholic. When we want our child to *have it better and amount to something* or to be a *chip off the old block*, we project our dreams and goals onto the child. Usually, this is done at a less crippling level of intensity with the non-alcoholic parent. It is always crippling, however, when done through alcoholism ego projection. This is due to the confused thinking of the drinking alcoholic. He will invariably have unreasonable expectations of the child and continue "molding" beyond reason.

The alcoholic is driven to accomplish something worthwhile if only through the child. The stable parent, however, does it for the child's benefit, but more importantly, recognizes when the child needs to develop his own personality. The acquisition process and effect of ego roles is different from that of defensive roles and requires further explanation. Let's suppose that Don, oldest of the Smith children, is invited to a slumber party, but there is a football game on television. In the past, Don watched the game with his father, John. He would yell and cheer for the home team along with his dad. While apparently having a grand time, both would be oblivious to other family members.

Sounds like fun, but it might be interesting to note that Don doesn't really care for football. Yet, he is compelled to go through this behavior because it is one of his roles. Incidentally, do you think Don will go to the slumber party, even though he really wants to? No way. That's kid stuff and for sissies. It is totally outside Don's role which is, by the way, John's alter-ego.

All role behavior, regardless of type, causes a loss of spontaneous action. Moreover, there is a withdrawal from any social interaction perceived as being outside the role. In other words, role behavior causes us to say only that which is preceived as being within the role. It is as though we were following some unwritten script, hence, the designation **role behavior**. On the other hand, it can prevent our doing things outside our role, even when there is a strong desire to do so. This can be readily seen in the above example depicting Don. All and all, role behavior is not only crippling to the family member, but also supports the alcoholic's continued drinking.

The alcoholic relies on the ego role and praises the behavior resulting from it. This gives the alcoholic self-worth and importance because, after all, it is an extension of himself. The defensive roles, however, are not as intensely ingrained. This is because they are not a direct reflection of the alcoholic and have very different dynamics within the support system. Also, he reacts quite differently with the family member subjected to defensive role action. Since he doesn't see this person as an extension of himself, the alcoholic will probably be critical in a negative way. Generally, the alcoholic blames, criticizes, ridicules, and sheds negative light on this person.

All members of the support system can fluctuate from one role to another from time to time. They will, however, be identified predominantly by one certain role. Following are a list of roles found within the alcoholic's support system. It is not an exhaustive list because the alcoholic will create new roles as his need for support dictates. Family roles, however, are better defined and predictable across all alcoholic families. They are presented first.

Victim: The alcoholic. This person is on a path of self destruction. A bold trait is his apparently selfish demands to satisfy his needs with complete disregard for others. He will have a negative effect on all within his social involvement. The degree of negative effect is directly related to one's closeness to him. The Victim, in later stages of alcoholism, is often disowned and avoided by others. If drinking does not cease, a lonely, drunken, shameful life will be terminated by early death. The role of the Victim is to do anything necessary in order to continue drinking.

Rescuer: (Usually the primary supporter) Either ego, defensive or a subtle combination of both roles. The Rescuer is closest to the alcoholic and trained well. This person is usually the alcoholic's spouse, but can be the parent, boss, other relative or friend. The Rescuer will be quick to understand the alcoholic's plight and feels that only he or she can truly understand or get through to him. The Rescuer plays the role of sage and advisor. He or she will be privy to the innermost secrets of the alcoholic and share most in his hurt. The Rescuer will take the alcoholic's side in most conflicts, loan him money and always get him out of jail. The alcoholic will also defend the Rescuer. There may be several Rescuers on the alcoholic's support staff.

Example: John comes home drunk, falls asleep on the couch and, sometime during the night, vomits all over himself and the couch. The Rescuer is awakened by John's nocturnal meanderings and proceeds to wash John, get him to bed, and clean the couch. The next

day, John awakens between two clean sheets without being aware of
his earlier sorry condition. The Rescuer also makes an excuse to
John's boss for John's inability to be at work the "morning after."
Finally, she points out to everyone how much better the couch looks
since she cleaned it. As a result of the Rescuer's intervention, John
was not allowed full confrontation with the negative aspects of his
drinking.

Prince/Princess: Ego role. Heir-apparent. This person is
groomed by the alcoholic to follow in his/her footsteps. This child
will more than likely be seen by the alcoholic as the one most likely
to succeed. Ironically, the Prince/Princess could be a thief, con-
man, doctor or truck-driver. It all depends on how the alcoholic sees
himself. Others will comment on how much like the alcoholic this
off-spring is. Prince/Princess can do no wrong and will be well
protected by the alcoholic.

Achiever: Combination of ego and defensive role. An Achiever of
greatness, he or she must accomplish things that will bring the family credit and positive recognition. The entire family will gain in
some way from the achievements of this family member and "bask"
in his or her glory. Through ego projection, the Achiever is driven to
play out the life role of the alcoholic's fantasies. The Achiever is
usually the oldest child and can be male or female.

   The alcoholic will identify with the Achiever and push him or her
toward accomplishing feats of which the alcoholic might have only
dreamed. The Achiever supports the alcoholic's drinking by the self-
perceived importance gained from these hollow achievements. The
alcoholic might say, "I'm not so bad. Look at my son...a doctor. I
must have done something right."

Family Clown: Defensive role. This is an important role within
John's support system. He or she will make a joke about everything.
This is especially true of anything that might bring John's drinking
behavior into a negative light. Behavior characteristics of the Clown
are always joking, never serious and always minimizing. Expressions of, "Oh, Mom, you know Dad wasn't serious," are common
with the Clown. John's drinking is supported by the *comedy relief* of
the Clown in a way that John is never brought to task for his irresponsible behavior.

Idiot: Defensive role. Can be any family member and does, in fact, fluctuate depending on the alcoholic's mood. Normally, the Idiot is an ego role relegated to the slowest thinker within the alcoholic's support system. Also, it will be primarily the one who disagrees most with the alcoholic. Of course, only an Idiot could possibly disagree with one as brilliant as the alcoholic. Behavior characteristics of the Idiot are slow thinking, incorrect responses (even when the correct one is obvious), trouble with school subjects and, of course, low grades. The Idiot will not accomplish anything of significance requiring brain power. The Idiot supports John's drinking through enhancing John's brilliant thinking by contrast. John does not have to confront his own stupidity. It is suppressed by his self-perceived brilliance in comparison to that of the Idiot. The Idiot also catches the blame for just about everything that goes wrong within the family.

Example: John comes home drunk, falls over the coffee table and breaks it. The next morning he confronts the Idiot. "See what you did, you idiot. You left your toy in the middle of the room and I tripped over it and broke the table." The child responds with, "I am sorry, Dad, and will not do it again." The alcoholic replies, "Well, okay. Here's a dollar. Go get yourself a soda." Had the child replied with, "I didn't do that. My toys are in their box," he probably would be ridiculed and whipped. The choice is an obvious one for a child to make.

Genius: Ego or Defensive role. The Genius must be right at all times. He or she will be a virtual walking encyclopedia of little used and trivial information. They will side with the alcoholic in all serious disputes which, according to the alcoholic, confirms their genius status. Ironically, this person will do well in school and probably be intellectually superior to others within the family constellation. The Genius supports the alcoholic by reinforcing the alcoholic's position. Also, the alcoholic gains an inflated ego from the Genius. After all, how could anyone but a genius parent one?

Placator: Defensive role. The Placator smooths ruffled feathers for John and tosses the olive branch before John actually confronts someone he has harmed. He or she runs John's interference by explaining just what the situation *really* is and what John *really* meant to say or do. The Placator has an exceptionally comfortable role in that he or she is hardly ever chastised by the alcoholic. The Placator, is John's confidant. Behavior characteristics of the Placator are patience, a level head, understanding, and an overall peacemaker demeanor. The Placator supports John's drinking by keeping the focus away from John's stupid alcoholism behavior. John allows the Placator freedom of interrogation and privy to John's personal thoughts to the extent necessary to make a good case.

Traitor: This is a tricky one. The Traitor is usually very close to the alcoholic and can be the number one supporter. He or she benefits from the alcoholic's dependent condition and strive to keep him dependent. The Traitor will pretend to want the alcoholic stable and in *control of life again*, but will do things to short circuit the rehabilitation process. The Traitor fears losing the alcoholic and holds on by using alcohol to do so. Male spouses will take advantage of an alcoholic wife sexually and in other ways by keeping her dependent on him and alcohol. The Traitor can also be a non-family member. In essence, anyone who gains in any way from the alcoholic's sickness fits the role. This is a subtle role and one that takes a keen eyed therapist to detect. A layman will invariably misinterpret the intentions of the Traitor. The husband of an alcoholic wife often plays the role of Traitor.

Of the many roles within the alcoholic's support system, a few were presented here. Specifically, there is within the alcoholic's family support system one primary ego role and several supporting defensive and lesser ego roles. The primary ego role is the one more perceived by the alcoholic as representing him or herself. This is the role that I refer to as either the Prince or Princess depending on the sex of the alcoholic and, of course, the child.

Each and every alcoholic will have at least two additional persons within his support system representing the **Rescuer** and **Placator**. Without the Rescuer, the alcoholic gets into trouble that he can't get out of without falling flat on his face or, at least, without causing a negative focus on his drinking. The Placator allows the alcoholic to get back into the good graces of those he wronged or shamed while under the influence. Added to these two basic supporting roles, the alcoholic can have many more within or without his immediate family. Each and every family member has a role by which he or she will be identified. Their roles can fluctuate from time to time but they will have a definite predominate role.

The alcoholic's life becomes more fantasy-like as the disease progresses and he begins to live out his fantasies through the family members. Mentally, he enacts his fantasies in sports, work, school, etc., while using the family members to accomplish his feats. His wife, for example, might be the strong confrontive person that he never was. The oldest son might be viewed as the brilliant student, the youngest son as the football player, the oldest daughter as the efficient girl Friday and the youngest daughter as the socialite. Through those closest to him, the alcoholic lives out his life's dreams. The extent of damage done by this process depends on the personality strength of the alcoholic plus the degree of sickness experienced by each family member.

As stated, all alcoholics project their egos. The children of alcoholics receive the ego and alter-ego projection with varying degrees of intensity and according to their level of sickness. In general, children of alcoholics are more receptive of this process than is the spouse because children's personalities are developing. Consequently, personality deformities experienced at an early stage of development react well to treatment if diagnosed accurately and caught early enough. If not, the personality deformities can severely impair the child's personal growth and development. If untreated, the adult child of an alcoholic will carry his personality deformity throughout adulthood. Moreover, the child will be at high risk to alcoholism himself. Therefore, ego projection analysis of each family member is essential in order to determine treatment needs. This is not the only problem. Coupled with role behavior is the previously mentioned flagrant and visible type of alcoholism *fallout*" affecting the entire family.

Direct fallout is recognizable in each family member as an inability to interact with others, especially at an emotional level that is real. They become unable to realize true emotions such as love, hurt, anger, fear, or shame. In other words, there is a defensive wall surrounding the feelings of each family member just like the one surrounding the alcoholic. These are the most obvious symptoms of direct alcoholism contamination, resulting from attempted heart to heart communication with the alcoholic. For the family member, it is like running into a defensive wall (see appendix). The emotional pain resulting from this experience causes an ego (see glossary) deflation. In defense, there is a wall built around the feelings of the family member in order to protect the ego from further damage. The communication process within an alcoholic family becomes a defensive wall to defensive wall one in which all interaction is false and robot-like. In other words, there is no real heart to heart caring and loving communication within this sick family.

Many therapists recognize these obvious symptoms of alcoholism and gear their entire family treatment program toward breaking down these defensive walls. This is only a tip of the iceberg and often conceals the other deep seated, alter-ego projected illness. In treatment, however, we occasionally need to treat the more obvious first and that is certainly true in treating the alcoholic family. This process can be likened to peeling a head of cabbage. We proceed one leaf at a time and eventually reach the core.

Treatment of the entire family is usually done at the same time. It consists of a three phase approach very similar to that explained in chapter three. You will recall that the alcoholic's treatment is often done inpatient while the family is most frequently treated outpatient. This is because the family member usually does not need separation from his environment like the alcoholic. There are times, however, when an inpatient program is advisable for the family member. Fortunately, more and more inpatient programs are becoming available for this purpose.

The goal of phase one therapy is to help each family member recognize his infirmity and the extent of it. The seriousness of his impaired emotional growth and development is also evaluated in phase one. Through this recognition, it is hoped that the individual will recognize the need for further treatment. As in phase one with the alcoholic, education is extremely important in treating the family. In most instances, the family was a part of phase one with the alcoholic and experienced significant education in that process. We do not, however, make any assumptions.

The entire family is asked to view presentations and each family member is required to do a written self-analysis. Each and every child old enough to do so is asked to write a paper about themselves. This is done without consulting any other family member beforehand. Within the paper, each member states how he sees himself within the family constellation. Role behavior is identified and an expression of feelings relative to that role is encouraged.

Individual counseling should be used sparingly. Usually, it is recommended in phase one if there is any indication of incest, or similar guilt-laden problems. These types of problems are generally difficult to bring out in group therapy during early group adjustment. As with treating the alcoholic, however, group therapy should be utilized as soon as possible. Once again, group therapy is the most effective way for the individual to break through his defensive wall. When indicated, therapy is intensified and focused more on restoration of the depleted self-images of each family member. The old defensive and projected self-images must be eliminated and real ones restored or caused to emerge. This is not an easy task! One would assume that the client would be anxious to drop role behavior and establish their real identity. Not so. Very often it is like pulling teeth to cause the giving up of certain phony and crippling roles. This is understandable because the roles have shielded the person from pain. After all, when the wall is penetrated and role behavior dropped, the client can now feel hurt again.

More importantly, the client can also laugh and feel real happiness and not have to engage in role behavior such as forced laughter. Of course, that is the sick type of baloney he has done for so long. Once the wall is dropped, however, he is also vulnerable to all other feelings. The recovering family member can now experience real love, hurt, fear, anger, etc., like never before. A concept difficult to comprehend is that one must be able to cry in order to really laugh. If you block out just one emotion, they are all blocked out.

The spouse must work hard in phase one, especially if he or she has been acting a dual role. The spouse is most often the **Rescuer**, but sometimes he or she is also a **Traitor**. Yes, as crazy as it might sound, this person could actually be sabotaging the alcoholic's recovery effort because his or her self-image is often so depleted. Moreover, the self-image and essence of the spouse is intertwined in the sick relationship with the alcoholic much like the prisoner who can't leave prison after years behind bars. One becomes a prisoner of their own dependency. The spouse fears losing the alcoholic husband or wife if he or she becomes stable and, therefore, independent. Consequently, the spouse either consciously or subconsciously wants the alcoholic to stay drunk and dependent. I see this mostly when the alcoholic is female and the male spouse is insecure. The female alcoholic invariably becomes so dependent that she is enslaved by her own support system. She becomes extremely dependent on the husband, who is usually her chief supporter.

The female alcoholic, especially, seems unable to leave her support and needs it even more as her disease worsens. She becomes totally dependent on her chief supporter. What power! The male spouse who is so insecure that he fears losing his wife if she gains independence will do "things" to keep her drunk.

A good example of this can be seen in the 1950's movie starring Susan Hayward called, "I'll Cry Tomorrow". The movie was based on the life story of Helen Morgan. She was a star of stage and theater during the 40's and 50's, and was identified in the story as being alcoholic. There is a scene in which Ms. Morgan was successfully rehabilitating from her disease. She was becoming independent, and not so dependent on her sick husband. He sabotaged her sobriety by forcing her into a stressful situation. He then conveniently gave her whiskey to "calm her shaking nerves". Shortly thereafter, she returned to her active alcoholic state and he, of course, to being her "slave master".

Often the spouse is not aware of being a **Traitor** and subconsciously does things to short circuit the alcoholic's rehabilitation effort. The damage is just as bad, however, regardless of intent or lack thereof. It is absolutely imperative that the therapist analyze spouse roles thoroughly. If the Traitor is one of those roles, corrective therapy must be applied immediately. Corrective action for the Traitor-spouse is to help him or her gain a positive self-image and the confidence that would preclude a need for such dependency. This takes expert therapy skills and can be extremely damaging to the client if not done properly. Obviously, this is a dual dependency. As the alcoholic begins to break free from it, the spouse pulls him back. As the spouse attempts the break, the alcoholic pulls him back. Consequently, they must get well together. It is often necessary, however, for the non-drinking spouse to take the lead. As defensive walls are destroyed and role behavior eliminated, the family member enters into phase two of recovery.

In phase two, we begin to either build or re-build the destroyed personalities of each family member. This is done primarily by determining the extent of the developmental gap and proceeding to close it. Phase three therapy is relegated almost entirely to reestablishing social intercourse. This is done much the same way as we did with the alcoholic. In fact, if the alcoholic is responding well to treatment and is ready for it, a merging of family therapy is done. Treatment in phase two and three should also be done in conjunction with Alanon or some other self-help group. Briefly, Alanon is comprised of recovering significant others of the alcoholic. There is Alateen and Alatot for the teenager and below respectively. It should also be emphasized that these groups are not a place to meet and just gripe or gossip. On the contrary, they are where serious recovering individuals share experiences of recovery and work out problems of mutual concern. Alanon is discussed thoroughly in chapter five.

By the end of phase two, defensive walls are penetrated and role behavior identified and at least partially eliminated. The **Achiever** learns that it is okay to fail; the Idiot learns that being smart is okay; the **Clown** learns not to laugh at life's sadness; and the **Rescuer** learns to allow others to be responsible for their actions. Through the treatment component of my EPA theory, all this is possible. It can be accomplished in a relatively short period of time. An alcoholic family can work through all three phases of treatment in roughly three months, if they are serious. The ultimate goal, of course, is to restore the sick alcoholic family to a stable, loving, caring and real family again.

Phase three therapy with the family is very enjoyable. This is especially so with the children who, generally speaking, respond well to treatment. Emotional walls are relatively easy to penetrate depending on the child's age and longevity of the problem. Role behaviors are probably most difficult to eliminate in the child if it is one of the *positive* ones. With patience, education and therapy, however, the child becomes healthy again. In phase three, we utilize many techniques of counseling as described in chapter three. Variations of psychodrama, for example, are used in order to eliminate role behavior and reestablish the real personality. Group therapy becomes more experiential in nature as the need to confront old anxieties is realized. Of course, the treatment component of my EPA theory is called *Experiential Therapy* and is just that. Nothing really happens, according to my theory, until it is experienced.

The entire family has, within the group setting, equal freedom of expression in order to reestablish real personalities. It is very important that old parental roles are dropped. In fact, all roles must be eliminated. Group members, especially the children, should not feel intimidated by old roles or anything else. Ideally, the group should meet in a different member's home each week in order that the experience will feel more authentic. This provides alternating families an opportunity to interact within a familiar and real setting.

Although emotional wall penetration usually occurs in phase one and certainly by the end of phase two, the opportunity to experience one's full emotional range may take longer. This process is speeded up, however, in phase three as true and real feeling confrontations are encouraged. No *patty cake* type of emotional interaction is permitted. Each group member is expected to say and demonstrate what he or she is really feeling. Statements such as, "Mom, I love you, but I will not be a counselor to you any longer; I am not comfortable with listening to your problems or trying to help you," or, "Dad, I really don't like football and will not watch the game with you every weekend," are often heard in phase three groups.

By this time, most all statements are really acceptable and the truth must prevail. This is real healing. Furthermore, hugs and demonstrations of love and affection are encouraged if real. Strictly forbidden is the phony or ritualistic hugging or talking of affection so prevalent within therapy settings. This type of phoniness is exposed immediately. We won't permit replacing one phony behavior with another. A phony hug, in my estimation, can be damaging. If the action of hugging is unacceptable just because you haven't done it for a while, then that's different. Try it, you'll like it.

This type of therapy is continued until a unification of each family is realized. There are situations, however, in which damage to the marriage aspect of the family is beyond salvaging. This often happens when the alcoholic spouse returns to drinking or is unable to stop at that time. Alanon efforts fail and the marital relationship terminates. Divorce adjustment counseling is then instituted with the entire family. In any case, the family must survive and not feel guilty in the process.

The spouse must be especially careful in future spouse selection because there is a strong propensity to remarry another alcoholic. Children of alcoholics also have a similar leaning because of the role behavior. Remember, each family member received feedback for their role behavior within the alcoholic family. Although all of this feedback was negative in the long run, it was attractive in a sick sense. This feedback was reinforcing, especially when, at the time given, it seemed positive. Therefore, unless therapy is successful, the family member will revert to another sick relationship. Also, developing a new and real personality takes work and is scary. It must be done or the same sick relationship will continue with every experience.

Characteristics of adult children of alcoholics are described within various books on the subject and are essentially correct. I take issue, however, with those who describe role behavior relative only to birth order. They delineate certain roles to *youngest male child*, *oldest female child*, *youngest child*, etc. Although certain defensive roles have a tendency toward sibling order, and ego roles are sometimes sexually determined, exceptions far outweigh the rule. Therefore, we must see this phenomenon as occurring without any definite pattern.

If we adhere to strict sibling order when identifying roles, then problems occur. A therapist might, for example, incorrectly identify a child's role based only on his birth order. In classic sibling role identificiation, the oldest male child must be the Achiever. Hogwash! I've too often seen the youngest female child or even the middle child as Achiever. Blanket acceptance that sibling order dictates a certain role can be damaging. Someone, invariably, will try to make the child fit the role and not vice versa. Overall, there is such a variation in role behavior and sibling position that I never assume because Donald is John's oldest son, his role will be . . .

There is at least one certainty about role behavior, however. Unless role behavior is correctly identified and eliminated, the victim will carry its characteristics to the grave. Likewise, he will more than likely exhibit all the sick behavior enroute. Emotional walls must be penetrated and real emotions brought forth or the victim will be emotionless except for phony exhibitions throughout his lifetime.

In concluding this chapter, a brief review will stress the importance of family therapy in treating alcoholism. As demonstrated, the entire family of the alcoholic suffers dramatically due to *fallout* from the alcoholic's sickness. Mostly a subconscious process, the contamination was identified as having specific role characteristics requiring treatment. Treatment consisting of three phases was suggested and a positive prognosis indicated. The building of emotional walls and the acquisition of role behavior was identified as a direct result of alcoholism in order to shield one from emotional pain. Furthermore, roles can be either alter-ego projections or defensive in nature. The former was identified as being a projection onto family members by the alcoholic and having a more conscious quality. Conversely, defensive roles were explained as being more of a subconscious process. All role behavior is damaging and requires treatment in order to identify and reestablish the real personality. Finally, a short discussion was presented on the damaging potential of preconceived ideas relative to role type according to sibling order or other factors. Overall, the importance of family treatment can not be overly emphasized. As the family *goes* and *grows*, so goes the world.

CHAPTER FIVE

SELF-HELP GROUPS

This chapter is relegated primarily to the recovering alcoholic and his or her family. It begins with everything you've always wanted to know about Alcoholics Anonymous (AA) but were afraid to ask. Next, the new AA member's concerns are addressed with valuable information aimed directly at helping the new member adjust to those first hectic days. Such questions as, "Do I have to give a lead?" or "What exactly does one do at an AA meeting?" will be answered. In addition, many valuable issues relative to early AA experience will be addressed. All AA members will find new insights into the Twelve Steps as the steps are analyzed one at a time in search of a clear and precise meaning to them. In addition, issues such as whether one should follow the steps in order or *jump around* with them are discussed.

My twenty plus years as a member of AA is shared with insights that promise to benefit all with their recovery effort. In addition, my views as a certified alcoholism counselor will be helpful to the confused AA member who falsely assumes that he or she should be counseled or do counseling at an AA meeting. Finally, I will explain

AA jargon which certainly confuses the new AA and probably causes problems with the long time member as well. The AA section will be followed by one on Alanon. The information contained within this section will be somewhat secondhand because my experience does not include being married to an alcoholic. My experience does include a close association with Alanon in the capacity of speaker and guest counselor on many occasions. Also, many of my clients are Alanon members and, of course, Alanon is recommended to all recovering family members. I feel this section will be most helpful to all those who are *sick* from alcoholism fallout and are tired of fighting the struggle alone. An excellent depiction of one's fears and doubts about going to their first Alanon meeting is presented. This is shared through a letter written by a former client. It is presented herein exactly as written and shows the process from the first meeting to wellness better than I could possibly do. It is sad, but real, and ends on a very high note. Any person who doubts Alanon involvement must read this letter. This chapter will conclude with more of my comments on self-help groups in general. This first section contains a selection of questions and answers about AA most often heard within my practice. They are the easy questions; they are also the ones asked by most new AA members. But what about the questions you are afraid to ask? Questions you are afraid to ask because you are too shy or you don't want to sound stupid, etc. These are the ones that really need answering. It is my guess that for every question asked by an AA member, there are at least double that many he or she is afraid to ask for one reason or another. We'll do the easy ones first.

"What is AA?" AA is such a vital component of recovery for so many alcoholics that I hesitate to give a personal definition. It is feared that I might fail to do it properly. Yet, in keeping with my promise to the reader that there will be no quoted text within this book, I offer my definition with a caution to the reader. If you are confused by my answer or in any way *turned off* by it, please read the forward to the Big Book "Alcoholics Anonymous". With that word of caution, I see AA as a worldwide fellowship of alcoholics comprising all races, religions, colors, ages, sexes and social status. AA members have one common goal which is the desire to stay sober.

It requires neither membership fees or dues nor is it allied with any person or thing. AA does not support any private or public controversies or groups. Also, it is not a religious organization nor does AA promote itself. Rather, it is sustained by attraction of those who find our commonality conducive to their desire to recover from alcoholism. All AA groups are self sustaining and survive by *passing the basket*. My definition also includes that, for me at least, AA can not be seen or touched, but is felt. It resides within us.

"What is the Big Book?" The Big Book is an easy to read work available throughout the free world. I will not try to explain its contents but encourage the reading of it. The book was originally published in 1939 when AA membership was a small fraction of what it is today. Its impact upon our alcoholic population can be partially realized by the fact that the Big Book, titled simply "Alcoholics Anonymous", has now reached millions of readers. Read it.

"What is an AA meeting?" Well, there are several different types of AA meetings. There is the classical closed meeting, an open meeting, a discussion meeting, and a Twelve Step meeting just to name a few. These will be explained in more detail since they are the more popular meetings within AA. It is felt that such explanation will benefit the new AA member because many new people avoid coming since they just don't know what to expect. There is probably nothing more scary to the early recovering alcoholic than the unknown.

A closed meeting is comprised of alcoholics only and, as the name implies, is closed to everyone else. The meeting is opened by a chairperson who asks everyone to stand and recite the Serenity Prayer. New members are sometimes uneasy because they don't know the words. Although this is a normal reaction, such fear is totally unnecessary because no one expects the new AA to know the prayer. In fact, the new AA member is not expected to do anything at his first meeting except be there. The Serenity Prayer is a very simple one that packs so much meaning for us all that I'll include it here for the reader's edification.

> God grant me the serenity
> To accept the things I cannot change;
> The courage to change the things I can;
> And the wisdom to know the difference.

Just pause for a moment and reflect on the meaning of these few simple words. I'll bet your blood pressure just dropped a few points after this prayer. The chairman welcomes all new members. New members do not have to do a thing. In fact, no one has to do anything at a meeting. We draw strength just from each other's presence. If you feel inclined to do so, however, you might stand

and say something to this effect, 'Hi, my name is Don and I haven't had a drink today. I feel . . . .'

After greeting the new AA, the chairman usually asks if there are any announcements from the floor. Those who want to announce their particular *home group* activities have the opportunity to do so. Any other information of common interest to AA is also welcome. No outside interests are accepted; i.e., "the west side little league women's auxilliary is having a bake sale" or any similar announcements are prohibited. The chairperson will then ask someone to read *The Twelve Steps, Twelve Traditions* and *How it Works*. I would suggest that new AA not be approached for this purpose. They might feel obligated to comply and yet be so nervous that they hesitate to come back. I can relate to this and will share from my personal experience.

In 1968, during my *struggle* (see chapter one), I was asked to read "How it Works". I didn't want to do this because I was scared, sweating and had no drink to settle my nerves. I felt obligated to read because all eyes were on me and the chairman was a friend. He incorrectly did this without asking me first. Although there are those who feel the best way to teach one to swim is to push them into deep water, I disagree. I read "How it Works" and felt terribly embarrassed. My voice cracked and my legs barely supported me through those agonizing five or six minutes. After the meeting, I went straight to a bar, got drunk and didn't get home for three days. I don't blame the chairman for my getting drunk. That was my decision. However, as a result of that incident, AA took an unnecessary beating within my thinking for a while. In fact, I was "gun shy" about meetings for a long time afterward. My ultimate fear about AA was that someone was going to ask me to give a lead (to be explained shortly). I didn't know that this was usually done in advance. My point here is that new AA are very nervous, insecure, shy and do not want to be focused on. They need to be brought out gently and at their own pace, with a little nudging, of course, at appropriate times.

One other comment on this subject might be helpful overall. My therapy sessions include an AA preparation component. I designed a technique used in phase one group therapy which has had excellent results. It's called a "mini-lead" in which each group member is asked to lead for ten minutes; an AA lead is usually an hour. As in all my exercises, clear demonstrations are made. We incorporate basic historical information about ourselves, such as, birthdate, place, marital status, children, work and a very brief history of our drinking. I've had group members threaten to *walk* rather than do this simple exercise, but with encouragement and a reminder that "this is therapy", they always do it. This is a good example of how scary a lead can be. Clients have given me feedback months later how that simple exercise helped them immensely in their first real lead. Now, back to our closed AA meeting.

The chairman next introduces the guest (lead) speaker for the night. He or she simply states their first name and proceeds to *tell it like it is*. Normally, the lead consists of the speaker telling how their life was while drinking without making a drunk-a-log out of it (see glossary); how they eventually found AA; and how life is now.

After the lead is concluded, the chairman asks for comments. At this time, those in the meeting have an opportunity to thank the speaker for his or her lead. If the audience member felt a special relationship with the speaker about a certain aspect of his lead, he usually will state as much. For example, the member might rise and say, "Hi Jan, my name is Don and I'm an alcoholic. I appreciated your fine lead. I can really relate to how guilty you felt by spending so much money on drink. As a result of my drunken spending, my family also suffered from lack of money." The speaker might reply, "You're welcome, Don. Thanks for your comment," or "Thanks for listening."

The purpose of the lead is to provide the speaker an opportunity to reflect on his horrible past just long enough to reinforce his need to remain stable. He or she can share with others how, through AA, they can enjoy today and hope for tomorrow. The audience benefits in many ways from the lead. They will be able to relive their experiences and realize that they are not the only ones to have done asinine things while under the influence. If new AA, they will gain hope for tomorrow. I feel it necessary to interject here that the hope for tomorrow is not planned sobriety for tomorrow. The entire concept of AA is one day at a time. We are never sober more than what we have today. I can remember, for example, that the thought of going a week without a drink would be absolutely mountainous. In fact, my early recovery was so traumatic that I would ask God for the strength to go fifteen minutes without a drink. Then it was *just one more hour* and, finally, I was able to go one more day. But, after more than ten years without a drink, I never consider myself as being stable more than one day at a time. The old saying that "yesterday is past and tomorrow may never come" really means just that relative to sobriety. All we have for sure is today.

The meeting is closed with the chairman asking everyone to stand

and join him or her in prayer. Following the meeting, everyone is invited to stay for fellowship and refreshments. Unfortunately, refreshments have always been in the form of coffee and donuts ever since I can remember. I say *unfortunately* because of the stimulating effect these "refreshments" have on us. It really doesn't make sense to serve such a combination of sugar, nicotine, and caffeine. The damaging effect this has on the alcoholic is difficult to measure. Before attempting to evaluate the damage, perhaps a better description of the problem is in order. First, we must accept that alcohol is a sedative which has caused a severe numbing action throughout the entire body. Secondly, it is necessary to recognize that alcohol is no longer providing our bodies sedation. This absence of alcohol-sedation is causing the nervous system to wake up dramatically. Any alcoholic will agree that when the alcohol dissipates from the system, the nerves are raw. I mean extremely raw. Why, then, do we need to stimulate ourselves anymore? Coffee is a stimulant; sugar (in the donuts) is also a potent stimulant; and nicotine (in the cigarettes) is equally as potent a stimulant. We are in essence taking raw and jagged nerves and doing the equivalent of rubbing them with sandpaper.

I can remember going to meetings before putting this all together and smoking like a fiend during the meeting. This would be followed by two or three cups of coffee while eating as many donuts. Then I would go home and be so *wired* that nobody could even talk to me without being yelled at or cut short. Sleep after these meetings was impossible because my brain would be racing ninety miles an hour. The next day, after falling asleep for an hour or so, my nerves would be in even worse shape because of the loss of sleep. I would drink more coffee to *calm* them only to have the opposite effect. My concentration at work would be impossible and I would just feel miserable overall. Of course, when an alcoholic in the early stages of recovery gets himself into such a state he knows what will take care of it—alcohol.

My intentions for mentioning this are not to make an excuse for drinking; there were other ways of working off such nervous energy. I could have jogged, for example, or played racquetball, but those things were not in my life at that time. Why do we put ourselves through the extra burden of caffeine, nicotine and sugar? Wouldn't it make more sense to have juice and fruit for our refreshments and reduce the smoking? It certainly would be healthier and might just add to our chances of staying sober.

Closed meetings are the backbone of the AA self-help recovery process. Other meetings are more complex and can offer opportunities for damage to the recovery of the early AA as well as to folks who have been around considerably longer. One form of damage is caused by what I refer to as "Coffee Cup Counselors". Many recovering alcoholics consider themselves responsible for those with less sobriety time than they. This is a normal attitude which develops because we care. Although it is within AA protocol to *take the message to others,* this should not be done within a counseling capacity. In my estimation, AA meetings were never meant to be training grounds for would-be counselors.

Even the professional counselor should not ply his trade at an AA meeting and, to the best of my knowledge, doesn't. The professional counselor knows better than to engage in such activity and, speaking for myself, is there for his own sobriety. It takes years of training and experience to be a qualified counselor and there are no short cuts. If you are interested in doing counseling then by all means go to college and learn how to do it. The best counselors of alcoholics are stable alcoholics with the proper education. The worst counselor is one without a proper educational background regardless of his or her alcoholism status. I can not stress this point too emphatically.

My advice to the young AA is to walk away (no, run away) from anyone who says, "Now the thing you ought to do is . . . ." The proper way to help is by sharing personal experience such as, "I had a similar problem and talked to my wife about it. It worked for me." Do you see the difference? The first person has the answer for you and probably does not understand the question. On the other hand, the second person does not have an answer for you, but shares what worked for him. There is a world of difference. Coffee Cup Counselors (CCC) are prevalent in AA and do tremendous damage. They mean well, but just do not have the educational background to practice a very complicated profession. They are really active at discussion meetings. This is a meeting in which recovering alcoholics supposedly discuss various problems relative to recovery. Unfortunately, these meetings become an "office" for the CCC to practice. He or she gives advice to all concerned about how to raise children, how to stay married or when to get married, what to do about financial problems and just about everything under the sun. My best advice to anyone just coming into AA or even if you've been around a while, is simply to walk out of such a meeting. In fact, I am opposed to such a meeting in the first place. AA is not founded on this type of activity. If your AA group is so inclined, however, hire a counselor to lead and facilitate these types of meetings. It will be the best money your group will spend for a while.

Another meeting in which CCC's are plentiful, but not quite as dangerous, is the Twelve Step meeting. Twelve Step meetings are comprised of recovering alcoholics for the purpose of clarifying and discussing aspects of the Twelve Steps (see appendix). Each person gives his or her opinion on various aspects of the steps such as whether they have to be done in order or not. While I am on the subject, this is an excellent time to introduce the steps.

It works best for me if I put the steps in the first person. For example, step one reads: "We admitted we were powerless over alcohol—that our lives had become unmanageable." All the remaining eleven steps were originally written in the third person. In other words, the pronoun **we** (third person) is used instead of **I** (first person). The steps written below are in the first person which makes them a personal issue for me. It might sound selfish, but when I go to these steps for help, my sobriety is my only concern.

Step One: "I admitted I am powerless over alcohol—that my life had become unmanageable." The foundation of my sobriety rests upon this first step. All alcoholics would like to think they can control alcohol, but we stable alcoholics know better. Even though my sobriety extends more than ten years, I would be drunk immediately if my thoughts convinced me that control were possible again. Oh, I could drink one the first night and maybe even the second, but sooner or later I'd be drunk again. I am powerless over the stuff. Ironically, my conviction of this simple fact came after my head cleared. In other words, I came to admit my powerlessness over alcohol after the fact. We mistakenly assume that the alcoholic must admit this before he can get sober. Not so. He must see it, however, before he can stay sober or gain stability.

The second part of Step One (that my life was unmanageable) must be ingrained. It is easier for us to see this because much of our mismanagement is recorded. Jail time, hospital time, divorce, auto wrecks, and fights are sad reminders of our mismanagement. By comparison we can see the before and after. I, for example, have not had a fight, been in jail, had a car wreck, etc., since sobering up.

Step Two: "Came to believe that a Power greater than mine could restore me to sanity." This is an extremely important step and sets the stage for Step Four. But that's getting ahead of myself. I glossed over this step for years and believe many of us do. My problem had to do with the word sanity. You'll recall from the prologue that the psychiatrists had just about convinced me of my insanity. Well, that scared me. Therefore, this step scared me. As I look back on my drinking days, there is no doubt that I was insane, but it was alcohol induced, not clinical insanity. There is a world of difference. The alcohol insane person's insanity clears with abstinence from all mood altering chemicals. Moreover, actual "insane" behavior occurs only when we are directly under the influence of the chemical. Let's now return to our discussion about the steps. Step Three will be discussed later. We will go to Step Four in order to make a very important point.

Step Four: "Made a searching and fearless moral inventory of myself." This step causes more conflict within the recovering alcoholic than any other. This is because he or she does not fully understand Step Two. Also, we are being as honest with ourselves and others as possible (honesty being the cornerstone of sobriety). In this effort, however, the young AA has a tendancy to be too harsh on himself and overly self-critical. They dredge up all those bizarre "things" that no one in a sane state of mind would do. Those things that caused shame to ourselves and loved ones become an obsession. They cause a moral and emotional conflict that rages within. Much of this can be avoided if you just make a proper Step Two and Three.

Step Two explicitly states ". . . a Power greater than myself could restore me to sanity." Clearly, insanity was a factor. We were definitely not mentally stable when we did these "things" (refer to Chapter One under the section discussing mental stability and especially mental brakes of the alcoholic). Now if one is insane, even for a certain period of time, during the commission of a crime, no court will judge him or her guilty. Why then do we do it to ourselves? It is because many recovering alcoholics have not really understood Step One and accepted their helplessness over the chemical. We were not only helpless over the chemical, but also led by it to a state of insanity. In other words, do you think you controlled the chemical and, therefore, had control over what you did? Give yourself a break—no way. Now let's look at **Step Three**.

"I made a decision to turn my will and my life over to the care of God as I understood him." This step further clears the way for a proper and complete Step Four and Five. The decision to turn the whole mess over to a higher power more than ever confirms our insanity while drinking. You will remember in Step Two that we came to believe that a power greater than ourselves could restore us to sanity. We followed this by doing Step Three. All of this adds up to our complete irresponsibility during our drunken behavior because of our temporary insanity. By this reasoning, doesn't it follow that we should evaluate ourselves in Step Four from the perspective of evaluating the morals of an insane person?

In my estimation, there is no other interpretation that we can make in all fairness to ourselves. Therefore, should an insane person be prosecuted for indecent exposure or urinating in the street? No. That should be the same line of reasoning used on ourselves when working through the steps. I have seen many an alcoholic return to drink simply because they can not close the door on the past. Using my reasoning and interpretation of these steps makes it much simpler. I believe this is the way they were originally meant to be read. It has taken many years for me to reach this conclusion.

Step Five: "Admitted to God, myself and another human being the exact nature of my wrongs." This can all be done simply by saying, 'God, you know I was drunk, my mind deranged and, in fact, insane when I did some things. I am not proud of those things and You, beyond humans, know it was not the real me who did them. From now on I am me and will be responsible. Not to say I'll be perfect. More than likely, I'll be getting back to You and ask forgiveness for something I will do intentionally in violation of my morals but, hopefully, not too many times." To *others* merely say, "Hey, that was another me. I am sorry if I offended you and I'll certainly strive not to again."

Step Six: "Was entirely ready to have God remove all these defects of character." This step is rather vague in my opinion but might be made simple by restating your desire to return to the pre-alcoholic person. Many of the defects of character, such as dishonesty, lying, stealing, uncaring for self or others, etc., are a direct outgrowth of the disease. The alcoholic invariably was a good person prior to being crippled by alcohol and through abstinence and therapy will return to that person. If, after sufficient time, one should still not be satisfied with one's goodness or certain personality qualities, they might redo Step Six. Yes, that's very permissible. In my estimation, one may return to a step and either affirm it or redo it. Whatever you feel is necessary. After all, it is your sobriety and stability at stake and you need to manage it accordingly.

Step Seven: "Humbly asked Him to remove my shortcomings." Once again, this is done in recognition of what has been said to this point. Also, it should be done after a few months of sobriety.

Step Eight: "Made a list of all persons I had harmed, and became willing to make amends to them all." Be careful with this one and the next. This step sort of cocks the hammer on a loaded pistol and Step Nine pulls it. Be sure of what you are doing here. First of all, reread the advice given regarding Steps One, Two, Three, Four and Five. Don't set yourself up to be "Johnny Squeaky Clean" at others' expense. First of all, are you sure you really harmed such and so or is it just your interpretation? Are you trying to be a martyr or is there really a need for talk with the other person(s)? The best way to make this decision is to evaluate your intentions. If you are too close to the problem, consult a counselor. Self-evaluation should address the question, "Who will benefit if I open this keg of nails?" If it is you, then your motivation is wrong. Let's evaluate an example in Step Nine. Which is, of course, the purpose for your list.

Step Nine: "Made direct amends to such people wherever possible except when to do so would injure them or others." This can be a *Catch 22*. In other words, it's damned if you do and damned if you don't.

The following scenario might clarify this concept. Let's suppose that during your drinking period of alcoholism and, as a result of the insane behavior already described as being inherent with alcoholism drinking, you committed adultery. You did this with another man's wife and were found out. There was a near divorce and break up of two families, yours and his. He decided not to confront you, sold his house and moved his family away from the likes of a drunken, crazy bum. Ten years later, you are sober and working your AA program. You come to Step Nine and remember the terrible thing you did and decide to make amends. Meanwhile, the other family weathered the storm, has one child in college and two in high school. The family as a unit is rejoined and is functioning well. Man and wife have worked through the incident many years ago and are in a good place. Should you reenter their lives on bended knee while apologizing for your madness and ask their forgiveness? Not in a pig's eye.

Your presence might reopen old wounds and feelings. You might cause a disruption that could be fatal to the marriage and family unit. Although amends would be made on your part, your conscious cleared and Step Nine completed, who suffered? Once again, if amends are primarily to make you feel better, forget it. You might just have to carry that one with you. Of course, if the steps were done properly and completely, then this should not be a problem. If you didn't, then go back and redo the ones necessary so there is harmony within yourself on this issue.

Step Ten: "Continued to take personal inventory and when I was wrong promptly admitted it." This one is not too difficult. I suggest you don't dwell on that "insane" time of your life and try being more flexible while growing. Although I have some difficulty *promptly* admitting when I am wrong, I do manage to do it. If I am wrong, that is.

Step Eleven: "Sought through prayer and meditation to improve my conscious contact with God as I understood Him, praying only for knowledge of His will for me and the power to carry that out." This is a personal thing with every human being. I call it *working on my spiritual recovery.* In my opinion, spiritual recovery is very important, but must be done at one's own pace. Don't join a church or become a born again anything until you are ready.

Step Twelve: "Having had a spiritual awakening as the result of these steps, I tried to carry this message to alcoholics, and to practice these principles in all my affairs." This is a very important step. First, be sure you have the message. Second, be sure you can communicate it to others in such a way that it will help them and not harm them. We sometimes lose sight that the best communication is not always by mouth. If you truly live AA and these steps, then someone will notice and might even try to emulate what you have done. If, on the other hand, you become well versed on reciting AA steps and jargon, attend all the meetings and don't really *walk your talk,* people will also see that. They will avoid you and what you are doing. In other words, carrying the message might be done best by just being an upright, sober and stable person.

Next question. "How many times should I attend AA?" That depends. Some say ninety meetings in ninety days for the new AA. For some, that works. For others, it is impossible. I evaluate each client individually and make recommendations accordingly. On the average, it is suggested that one attends three meetings per week in phase one, two a week in phase two and one a week in phase three. These are minimum required meetings. The client, of course, is free

to attend extra meetings as he or she feels it necessary. It is important that one does not become addicted to AA, however.

AA is a definite factor to be included in one's sobriety effort. It
must be realized, however, that one does not get sober for AA but
AA helps one to get sober and then stable. We must be aware of the
possibility of getting addicted to AA or anything else. I have seen
clients go to AA meetings every night for long after it appeared to
be needed. Also, there are those who sacrifice all family and social
life to attend meetings. As a stable alcoholic, one gains a new life or
regains an old one. Either way, one must become spontaneous, free
and yet responsible.

This includes, of course, a sound unification of family and social
obligations that should include some variety and not just AA. If, for
example, one's daughter is graduating from high school, he should
not miss it just because it is "AA night" and he is afraid someone
will notice his absence. This will draw flack from those who see AA
as a weekly or nightly ritual. In my estimation, AA is not meant to
interfere with life, but to help one get on with it. AA is there for us
when we need it, not we there for it. Once a person has finished
phase three therapy, they can choose how much or how little AA is
necessary.

"What is a sponsor?" A sponsor is someone who has at least one
year of sobriety and, hopefully, is a stable alcoholic. He usually
frequents AA and is familiar with all its principles and works. The
sponsor makes himself available to the new AA in helping him
make the transition from bar to AA. Also, he acts as a sounding
board for the new AA and shares his own experience. Moreover, the
sponsor helps the new member recognize the need for counseling
when issues are too deep for the sponsor. In a sense, the sponsor
sort of takes the new AA by the hand and leads him until he can
find his own way.

The above questions are frequently asked in and around meetings. Now we look at a few questions most AA members never hear
because the new AA usually thinks the questions might sound stupid. There is nothing more sensitive than the person just coming
into AA. For that reason, I normally hear the following questions
within the privacy of my office.

"Will I be asked to give a lead?" Not until you are ready and
normally not within the first year of recovery. Your sponsor will
probably be the first to know when you are ready. At that time he
might discuss the subject with you. Under no circumstances should
you be scheduled to lead unless you are consulted and perfectly

willing to do so. Giving a lead is not necessary in the recovery process and I personally know several recovering alcoholics with quality stability who have yet to give a lead and have no intentions of doing so. Be aware that unless you are a public speaker, the thought of leading is anxiety provoking. This is normal and unless you absolutely don't want to lead, you might want to make yourself do it and forego the anxiety discomfort. By the time you are ready, you will realize that many of us will never win a toastmaster's trophy, but we *tell it like it is*. That's all we can do and all that is expected.

"How long do I have to talk if I give a lead?" Once again it depends on the individual. I've heard some very good leads take only fifteen minutes. On the other hand, some take an hour and a half that would have been better if shortened a little. You can ask certain people, "How's the weather?" and it will change three times before they completely give you an answer. Take as much time to say what you need to say is my best advice. The average lead is approximately one hour. The old speaker's rule of thumb applies: stand up, speak up, shut up and sit down.

"Can I attend a meeting if I've had a drink within the same twenty-four hour period?" Twenty years ago I would have answered this question with an absolute no. Today, however, your desire to stay sober is seen as the only criterion to attend a meeting. Generally speaking, an alcoholic decides either to drink or do something else. Hopefully, the something else would be an AA meeting. I've seen semi-intoxicated people show up at meetings who might have thought they couldn't force themselves to attend otherwise.

Attending the first meeting, even if drunk, might help someone start a path of sobriety leading to quality stability. I've seen inebriated persons "stagger" into a meeting, satisfy their curiosity and leave immediately. Even this latter person, in my estimation, is reaching out for help. We should view his behavior accordingly. The alcoholic who decides drink is an answer, but realizes after taking one that he was wrong, is not rare. In my estimation, we should welcome him for having sense enough to quit drinking and attend a meeting. If he is drunk and just wants to disrupt the meeting, ask him to leave. If he doesn't, call the police. At least he won't cause an automobile wreck while in jail. Besides, it might do him some good to wake up in jail. It might sober him up.

"I hear so often that sobriety is only one day at a time. Why, then, do so many people seem anxious to tell me how many weeks, months, or years they have gone without a drink?" This is a good question and I'll try to answer it objectively. This is difficult to do because I, too, am guilty of *letting the cat out of the bag* about my length of sobriety from time to time. First of all, I think we do it because we are proud of not drinking and are, in a sense, bragging about it. I will use my sobriety time in a treatment sense to let clients know that it is possible to function not only day after day, but also year after year without alcohol. But getting sober and staying that way is a one day at a time process.

An important aspect of this subject is that getting drunk or falling off the wagon is also a one day occurrence. I've seen those with long sobriety time who, for whatever moment of weakness, take a drink. He then goes into what I refer to as a catastrophic syndrome. He feels that his sobriety time is gone and he might as well forget the whole thing and *drink till I die.* This is so absurd. If I get drunk tonight, I hope my thinking would be straight enough tomorrow to not drink. The drunken night would be over and a new day of sobriety beginning. This is very important. Reread in chapter three the section on relapse.

"Should I tell others that I am an alcoholic?" Only if you want to. As you gain stability, your views on alcoholism will change. Of course, there is a very large segment of the population who do not understand alcoholism and have old-fashioned ideas about it. They might look at you in a negative light because of their fears and biases. That's their problem. Until you have confidence and strength enough to tolerate this type of closed mindedness, you might want to confide only in those who understand. Recovery from alcoholism is something to be proud of, but staying drunk isn't.

"There seems to be a secret language among AA people. It was disturbing to me at first because I was always contradicted. I said I felt fine and was told, 'no, you don't.' I said I quit drinking and was told, 'no, you haven't, you're just not drinking today.' Should I learn all these catch phrases and say them?" Not unless you want to, but please, don't make the same mistake. As you know, new AA are very sensitive. Unfortunately, a few AA members are anxious to tell you how to talk, act and feel. Compliance with such effort is just that, acting. Be yourself. Once again, these people mean well and you probably don't know how fine you'll feel in another day. Comparatively, you don't feel fine. Tomorrow or a month from now you'll feel so much better that you can't possibly feel fine today. I believe that is the point the AA member is trying to make. Unfortunately, this abrupt challenging and confrontive attitude doesn't sit well with many new AA. It turns them off and chases them away. In that early stage of recovery, we don't need much of an excuse to get drunk anyway.

"What is a pigeon?" This is a new AA member who is still being *bird dogged* by a sponsor. The term is not meant to reflect negatively on the new AA and can be compared to "rookie" as used in most sports. Bird dogging is a term not used as much as it once was and refers to the sponsor's effort to help the new AA. The sponsor will call the new AA at first to remind him of the time and place of a meeting. He will also provide transportation to the new AA if necessary. Generally speaking, the sponsor will do much more to ensure meeting attendance during this bird dogging period. The sponsor will gradually withdraw his involvement. Eventually, it is, "I won't call you; you call me if you need me," type of relationship.

"Am I obligated in any way to do anything in conjunction with the meeting either before or after?" Absolutely nothing. The secretary sees to all the nuts and bolts of the meeting, such as coffee making, donut buying, etc. He might ask everyone who is willing and able to fold up chairs after the meeting. As a new AA, you are not even allowed to donate the customary dollar after the meeting. This continues for usually the first thirty days of sobriety. Like the saying goes, "No obligation and no salesman will call."

This concludes the question and answer section which was presented as a means of explaining AA from a common sense perspective. It makes sense also that AA is changing in many ways. After some twenty years of AA involvement, I can say that the average age of AA members has reduced dramatically. At twenty-eight, I was easily the youngest AA in many of my first meetings. Today, it is not unusual to see many folks in their teens and early twenties at AA meetings. Moreover, twenty years ago Springfield, Ohio, had one meeting a week. Today, there is a meeting at least every day of the week and often as many as two or three in one day. There is, for example, the morning meeting, lunch meeting and the traditional evening meeting occurring all in one day. AA has come out of the closet and what's more important, alcoholism led the way. This leads to my final comment about AA.

What I am about to say will astound the reader and especially the old AA member. Read it through carefully before forming an opinion. Remember that my relationship with Alcoholics Anonymous spans twenty years and I have the utmost confidence in its self-help concept. I believe, however, that it is time we eliminated the word anonymous. That's right. I suggest we alcoholics stop contributing to our own shame and rejection by the public. We strive for acceptance and yet we hide in order to meet. In addition, many times we do not reveal our identity. Alcoholism is a recognized disease that more and more people are accepting without stigma. So why do we, the alcoholic, hide behind anonymity?

The need to be anonymous is no longer valid. Years ago employers and others could discriminate against alcoholics. We were seen as immoral, indecent and wicked. It was necessary to conceal our disease because of such archaic ignorance and "holier than thou" attitudes. Thanks to the bravery of such people as Betty Ford, the late Marty Mann, and others, however, the stigma is lifting. President and Mrs. Reagan have endorsed treatment for alcoholism, not punishment. We are at the cutting edge of a total acceptance of alcoholism without stigma. Therefore, it is time we in AA did as much for the acceptance of alcoholism.

I think it is time that the word *Anonymous* be dropped from the name of Alcoholics Anonymous and changed to *Allied Alcoholics, Accepted Alcoholics* or *Admitted Alcoholics*. This way, we maintain the so popular "AA" designation but drop the stigma in every concept. Everything remains the same except we eliminate the word anonymous. I, for one, am not proud of being alcoholic, but I most certainly am not ashamed of it. Let's do our part and quit bringing further stigma on ourselves. How can we expect understanding and acceptance when we do not project an image worthy of it?

I'll be the first to recognize the danger in fooling with something that has worked so well for such a long period of time, but just think how much better it could be. For some fifty years AA has remained essentially as you know it today except for the splinter groups. Step discussions, breakfast, lunch and dinner meetings are a relatively new addition to AA meetings. I think it is good to change in order to improve visibility. Who knows how much a positive effect these additional types of meetings have on the skeptic who can't decide about AA? Also, the family or open meetings have contributed to our positive visibility. In closing this section, I would like to reiterate that I have very strong feelings that the removal of anonymity is now needed if alcoholism is to receive full respectability as a disease and more global acceptance.

No longer would there be a need for self-discrimination and concealment. This in itself would probably attract even more of our number. Respectability means a lot to most people. It is conceivable that those who have never attended a meeting view alcoholics as low life or a bunch of bums. They certainly would be justified in thinking that way because their view would be based on the street drunk. Add to this the fact that we meet anonymously and we, ourselves, contribute to such an image. "Their opinion isn't important," you might say. Once again, you are right. But supposing that person was trying to decide whether to come to us for help or not. Presently, we might just scare him away. If we projected a better image, however, he or she might join us. There are millions more who need the help available from the principles of AA and we would be wise to reach these people. Also, it wouldn't hurt to shed more positive light on ourselves as individuals.

We now turn our attention to Alanon. Alanon, like Alcoholics Anonymous, is a self-help group. It consists primarily of spouses and families of alcoholics but also welcomes close friends, employers, neighbors, etc., of the alcoholic. In other words, Alanon is for the non-alcoholic sufferer of alcoholism. The main thrust of Alanon is to provide those who suffer from this type of alcoholism a commonality in which understanding, relief and hope for a better life might be realized. This is accomplished through self-help types of meetings in which experiences are shared, clarification made and better understanding gleaned. Through Alanon, a better understanding of the alcoholic and his or her disease is sought. More importantly, a better self-understanding by the non-alcoholic sufferer is sought. Through this understanding, it is hoped that one's life can be turned around. Alanon offers an alternative from the alcoholism path of destruction to one of normalcy and respect.

Like AA, Alanon meetings are structured around the Twelve Steps and Twelve Traditions. Every meeting is opened with the Serenity Prayer and closed with prayer. It, however, is not a religious group, per se, nor is it allied with any particular race, religion, color or creed, but open to everyone worldwide. The only requirement for membership seems to be that of a desire to break the sick and dependent relationships established with alcoholism and become a self-willed human again. This and all other observations relative to Alanon are mine and do not necessarily reflect those of The Alanon World Service Office.

I am not a member of Alanon because, as you know, I am alcoholic. That is not to say, however, that an alcoholic can not belong to Alanon. On the contrary, being alcoholic does not preclude us from also experiencing problems of alcoholism as described above. This is especially true after reaching stability as an alcoholic. In fact, many alcoholics find help within Alanon to help them deal with an alcoholic spouse, family member, etc. Personally, I have not needed this type of help. My experience with Alanon is limited to being guest speaker at meetings on several occasions and following the process of my non-alcoholic clients who suffer from alcoholism fallout. All of these are referred to Alanon.

Typical non-alcoholism thinking relative to Alanon and other aspects of alcoholism can be best depicted in the following letter. It was written by a former client who graciously consented to my request of her to share with us her experience. It is shared here in its entirety with her permission:

My first Alanon meeting was a disaster. I knew that I was involved with an alcoholic, but wasn't fully convinced yet. The alcohol related problems were not all that serious and they were spaced apart. They didn't happen every day or even every week. Even so, I knew something was wrong and suspected alcohol was at fault. I don't recall how I learned of Alanon, but somehow became aware of when and where they met. I was nervous at that meeting, but confident that this was the way to stop him from drinking or, at least, get him to control it. I did not understand alcoholism.

During the meeting, I started feeling that I didn't belong there. These people had problems and they were serious ones. My reason for being there seemed very petty. I was not being beaten, in financial trouble, or had lost a job. Having always been a strong-minded, independent person, I started thinking that I could handle my problems without help. The others needed Alanon, but I didn't. I just needed to work harder on solving my own difficulties.

After the meeting, a well-intentioned lady tried to convince me of the entire Alanon program in one easy lesson. I understood very little of what she said. At one point, she asked if the alcoholic ever hit me. A little shocked, I said, "No, of course not." Her reply was "Well, he will." I thought she must have been crazy. How could she predict someone's actions, especially when she didn't know the person? The realization that alcoholics are predictable came much later. I was never physically beaten, but the alcoholism became much worse. That is what she had tried to tell me.

For two years, I worked harder at controlling my *problem,* the alcoholic. As a result, I became sicker. Trying to control the alcoholic caused me to lose control of myself. I had no idea that my efforts were going the opposite direction of my intentions. This was a difficult lesson to learn. Equally difficult was the inner fight with my pride to be able to admit that I was making matters worse.

During my *struggle* downhill, many things happened to me. I broke my own wrist out of frustration, anger and despair. I received a bad review at work (the first) due to my attitude, became overweight, lost friends and eventually, lost my job. Also, many nights were spent worrying about or arguing with the alcoholic. My temper was out of control. I screamed and yelled at the alcoholic when he was there and even when he wasn't. I threw things, broke things, hit things and even threatened to jump out of a car to try to prove my point to the alcoholic. I was stubborn, but thank God, I finally proved something, but to myself. My own sanity was in serious trouble. I, myself, needed help.

The counselor at the local mental health clinic talked of anger and other things. Very little was said about alcohol's effect on everything, yet, Alanon was suggested. I felt even worse. The hospital clinic for substance abuse did not help either, but they, too, suggested Alanon.

Fear of getting worse was now my main concern. I had to do something to help myself in any and every way possible. I was desperate. I had found a good job, but knew my work performance wasn't as good as it could or should be. Alcohol related problems consumed my whole life. I was scared, ashamed and couldn't understand what had happened to me. I was not myself. It was almost as if an evil force had taken over my soul.

Once again, I found out where and when Alanon met. The parking lot was as far as I could make myself go. I sat in the car and cried, hoping someone would come to me. This went on for about a month. Now, in looking back, I realize Step One of the Alanon program was taking place in that parking lot. I was admitting my powerlessness over alcohol and that my life had become unmanageable.

Thank God, I found the strength to go in one night. That night there was a special lead. My mind was spinning and could not concentrate on what was being said. I wanted to leave early, being afraid someone would speak to me and I would cry. When I managed to slip out, my intentions were not to go back.

The next week found me in that parking lot again. Since there was nothing else to do, I went in. This time it was a discussion meeting. I don't know what was said, but it was all I could do to keep the tears from flowing. I could sense a warmth in that group of people. It was like lightning bolts of love zapping across from person to person. There was such caring and understanding, and no one was pointing their finger saying, "you did wrong". Everyone here was accepted as they were and loved, but I was on the outside looking in. I felt like a little beggar looking through a window at a family sitting down to a huge meal.

Was it possible for me to share in that? It didn't matter if it helped the alcoholic or not; I needed that for me. Alanon was like a magnet to me. Was I imagining the warmth and caring? No, there it was again. Some of these people actually seemed happy. I reasoned that they couldn't have alcohol related problems like me. Yet, why were they there? Were they just having a good time? That didn't make sense. I wanted to see more. I became anxious for the meeting time to come, and hoped the alcoholic wouldn't interfere. There was now a little, tiny something to look forward to. There was something that held a glimmer of hope for me, alone. The alcoholic refused to recognize a need for help, but I was going to take advantage of all the help I could get.

Thank God, no one pressed me to talk at first. Little by little, I was able to open up and share myself. It was hard to do, but the people there didn't criticize, laugh, or show pity. They listened, understood and cared. They gave me love and a reason to hope. It was hard to accept, but they also gave encouragement and taught me patience.

My sickness didn't happen overnight; it would take time to get well. I learned to look for the positive side of things. Sometimes it was necessary to look hard and search it out. It was even harder not to stare at the bad side. I re-learned how to hang on.

Slowly, I became able to relate to these people and their thoughts and feelings. I was no longer alone. When a crisis at home happened and I needed help, I could count on an Alanon member. When I was hurting inside and needed to talk, if it took all night in an Alanon member's kitchen, it was okay. When I was too scared to go to the police, but knew it was the right thing to do, Alanon went along to hold my hand while I took care of unpleasant, unfamiliar business. Alanon could not and would not solve my problems for me. There still were terrible times to go through, but Alanon supported me in working things out. Alanon also put the emphasis on my real problems which were my own attitudes, feelings, and behavior.

Alanon wouldn't let me blame the alcoholic. Of course, he played a significant role in my life, but my reactions to his drinking were not his fault. I, alone, had to take responsibility for my behavior. I did not like my behavior, but I had the ability to change that. Another lesson learned was that I, too, was a victim of the disease of alcoholism.

The concept of the Serenity Prayer was difficult to learn. *God grant me the serenity to accept the things I cannot change; courage to change the things I can; and wisdom to know the difference.* It was not possible to change the alcoholic although I wanted to. It was hard to regain the courage to change myself. This realization meant surrendering an assumed *power* or control over anything or, more importantly, anyone else. These were painful lessons, but I was learning about life. Alcoholism became secondary; my life became foremost.

From Alanon I gained hope of becoming well and returning to the person I used to take pride in being. However, I felt that I was still sick. Important as Alanon is, it isn't enough. Alanon is like an umbrella to shield you from the miserable rain, but I wanted to come in out of the rain.

That's when the decision was made that I needed professional help in order to fit the pieces of my puzzled life back together in earnest. Alanon supported this decision, but an interesting thing happened. The people who gave me the best support and help during the miserable times were not able to provide the kind of support needed as I was growing and changing. Those first supporters said things like, "You're not well yet. There will be more bad times. This is a lull in the storm."

Luckily, my group was large enough that there were others who could see my growth. They appreciated and encouraged it with comments like, "What you're doing is agreeing with you. You look years younger." This helped to strengthen the courage needed to continue the changes I was making through therapy. Negative comments caused me to question myself. I needed a positive outlook to *keep the faith.*

Alanon had taught me to cope with my problems, but it could not provide the solutions to those problems. Only through therapy and tremendous effort was I able to make the necessary inner changes that brought my life from barely tolerable to happy again. Having faith in my counselor helped to speed up this process.

Faith is another thing Alanon promotes. I took the chance to try to turn my will over to the care of God. My previous efforts, trying to force my will on others, wasn't working. Yet, it seemed risky to release my will, give up the fight, and let the chips fall where they may. In other words, let God take control. It didn't seem like an adult decision to give in to fate. However, when I am able to do exactly that, life in general becomes easier, calmer and, surprisingly, not such a traumatic or dramatic problem after all. If this were the only thing I received from Alanon, it was worth all the time and effort put into working its program.

After becoming comfortable with the group, I chaired our meetings for a month. I'm glad I did, because doing so helped to set my convictions and boost my confidence.

One of the closing comments to an Alanon meeting is, ". . . take what you like and leave the rest." Not everything I heard was valid information or advice for me. No group, just like an individual, is perfect. I was able to listen and sort out what was said and, as a result, I discovered much that applied to me.

Clearly, the new Alanon enters with apprehension and misgiving. This is perfectly understandable if we consider that the family member's sickness is a subtle one. It is a sickness that creeps into one's innards without the victim being aware of it. Read again chapter four. Remember, the new Alanon is plagued with self-doubt, shame and guilt. Invariably, he or she has not yet sorted anything out. They actually feel responsible for not only their own complications but also the alcoholic's as well. It is extremely difficult to break from these erroneous beliefs even though they are causing most of one's suffering. The process from sick to well is extremely painful and difficult for significant others and closely parallels that of the alcoholic's.

It is absolutely gratifying beyond word description to watch the transition of the client from a demeanor of absolute dejection to elation. The person enters your office a symbol of helplessness and hopelessness. They invariably are depressed which is masked by cynicism and psuedo (false) anger. All the outward symptoms of alcoholism contamination are there (see appendix). In a few short weeks, however, all that is reversed. Alanon can play a major role in this process. But, like AA, there are precautions.

The new Alanon member must be aware of the *fixer* and other people who, although well meaning, can be damaging. They are ready to *tell* you how to do it. They will listen with obvious concern and yet not listen because they already *know* what you need. This is the fixer. He or she will have the answer without understanding the question. Rather than sharing what worked for them and allowing you to make decisions for yourself, they will take charge. Invariably these people are frustrated as their easy solutions only complicate matters more.

There are also Coffee Cup Counselors in Alanon and, just like in AA, are just as damaging. Further, there is the bleeding heart who will wallow in and thrive on your sorrow. Moreover, the *tyrant* who is out for revenge is found in some groups. They will condemn the alcoholic while verbalizing ways to get even with that "no good so and so". My advice is to avoid interacting with anyone who is obviously sicker than you. Of course, this is difficult to perceive in your early recovery. Therefore, a good counselor is necessary to help you sift through what is therapeutical for you and what is damaging.

In general, Alanon groups should be compassionate, understanding and supportive. There should be discussions of alcoholism contamination and family hardships. Moreover, these talks should be directed in an effort to define alternatives and possible solutions. If the group seems directed toward vindictiveness and revenge, then you might want to look for another group. Alanon is not designed for such pursuits, but, alas, these groups are all too prevalent. I would not recommend continued membership if the predominant theme centers around condemning the alcoholic and ways in which to get even. Furthermore, if hatred and vindictiveness are encouraged or allowed to continue as a rule, then leave.

In addition, Alanon meetings should not become a sewing circle type of gossip meeting. Also, strict confidentiality of other members should be adhered to. A good rule of thumb is not to engage in conversation about any member not present. Finally, don't let your group become a *pick up* haven. There are those who attend Alanon and AA to find a male or female friend. They prey on the misery of others and use the vulnerability of Alanon and AA members. They are there selfishly and often in order to further their own efforts to meet and take advantage of the opposite sex. AA is not a lonely hearts club. We call this distastful behavior "thirteen stepping". In essence, thirteen stepping means attending a meeting or carrying on any activity in the name of AA or Alanon for reasons other than sobriety. Freeloaders who only show up at "eaten' meetens", for example fall within this category. They only attend meetings where free food is served. If a person is destitute and needs something to eat, then he or she is welcome, but you see many familiar faces at these meetings and at no other time.

Relative to the above discussion is a final point, alcoholics should not date alcoholics. All too often I've seen this happen even though it is discouraged. Although it is possible for two alcoholics to date or marry one another and remain sober, it is highly improbable. The relationship is started with the best of intentions. It is reasoned that joint efforts toward a common goal is better than one. In other words, the alcoholics think they can help each other stay sober. I have yet to see this work in all my years of practice. Usually, one or the other will get drunk and no matter how hard the sober member tries to stay sober, he or she follows suit.

It really stands to reason that if you are around a drinking person long enough, especially sleeping with one, then you, too, will drink. Therefore, it is wise not to date another alcoholic. This is the reasoning behind Article III of my original contract (see appendix). Simply, it states that I would never again date a lady who has more than two drinks in any one evening while on a date with me. It is assumed that she is either too uncomfortable with me or alcoholic. Either way, I don't need it. Exceptions to this rule might be considered if each recovering alcoholic has at least five years of sobriety. It's still very risky in my estimation.

Any discussion about self-help groups would be incomplete without talking about halfway houses. Although one might not expect it, residents of these establishments often depend strictly on each other for recovering support. A halfway house is a residential facility where recovering alcoholics can find a sober atmosphere in which to continue putting their lives back together. Halfway houses are almost entirely self-sustaining by the recovering alchoholic residents. They each pay a minimal room and board fee which usually ranges from twenty-five to a hundred dollars per week. This will depend on overhead and other expenses, but is always at a minimum. Most generally, the facility is a nonprofit one and funding might be supplemented by local or federal monies. If so, the alcoholic without funds is provided a place to work on his recovery free of charge until he finds a job.

Often, the alcoholic, if uninsured, is referred to these facilities direct from an acute care hospital. In this case, the acute care facility will have monitored his immediate withdrawal from alcohol. More often than not, however, the alcoholic is admitted right off the street or referred by a private practioner. One's length of stay in a halfway house varies from a few days to many weeks depending on several factors.

Professional involvement of social workers, counselors and medical staff varies from none to elaborate depending on funding available. Invariably, the recovering residents provide their own needs in these areas supported only by a strong AA involvement. Ironically, alcoholism recovery seems highest in houses where professional involvement is minimal. This might be due to a greater acceptance of responsibility for one's own recovery rate when no one is *pushing*. Unfortunately, however, other needs such as social, medical and counseling might be neglected. Of course, volunteer workers in all health care areas find halfway houses an excellent area to sharpen their skills. My first official counseling experience was in such a setting and had a strong influence on my present career. Normally, a house will have at least two or three permanent staff members.

Entry into a halfway house is generally done on a first come and space available basis. A social history is taken and, where possible, a medical examination is made. The recovering alcoholic is admitted on a probationary status and is expected to conform to house rules. These rules are always headed by "no intoxicating liquids or other drugs will be taken during your stay either inside or outside the house." Of course, exceptions are permitted for certain lifesaving drugs such as insulin, but rarely are tranquilizers permitted no matter who prescribes them. The resident is cautioned that violation of this number one rule will result in his immediate discharge. Also, there are other rules and regulations which must be followed. Moreover, each house will vary to some extent, but all will include rules relative to cleanliness, fighting, morality and AA. All residents take turns cleaning various house areas and cooking if no permanent cook is on staff.

In addition, each resident is expected to work toward stability by regular AA attendance and maintaining a structured lifestyle. Halfway houses are not *flop* houses where drunks lay around all day. On the contrary, every one is expected to be actively involved in their recovery. Usually, committees are set up on a continually rotating basis in which each resident's progress is monitored. Also, there are usually weekly community meetings within the house in which concerns are discussed. Invariably, structured counseling is performed daily in which all residents share their individual recovery progress with each other. Often the person with the longest sobriety time (see glossary) will lead these counseling sessions. Volunteer professionals are welcomed if they meet both of two criteria: 1) if they are really sincere in wanting to help, and 2) if they know what they are doing. This second requirement can be temporarily waived if the professional is willing to learn.

I must say that we need to look positively toward more halfway houses as alcoholism rehabilitation sites. Although the more elaborate acute-care facilities offer more in the way of services, the cost is becoming prohibitive. A month's stay in a halfway house might cost at most five hundred dollars (often much less) for each resident. Compare this with the ten thousand dollar expense for the same length of stay in an acute care hospital rehabilitation unit. This is certainly out of balance from an economic perspective. Intensity and level of care are much superior within the acute care setting, but is it always necessary?. Within these more elaborate setings, the client is assessed daily by a small army of professionals. This includes the medical doctor, psychiatrist, psychologist, social worker, counselor, and ancillary professions, such as nursing. No doubt, all his needs are evaluated and serviced without his ever leaving the treatment unit. The question might be whether or not every recovering alcoholic needs such elaborate professional involvement for his entire treatment program. Medical needs, for example, are often non-existent or minimal after detoxification. Psychiatric services and psychological testing is almost counter productive within the first three months of recovery (see chapter three).

Why not evaluate the needs of the alcoholic within a one or two week inpatient setting and treat accordingly? My EPA theory with its three phase treatment plan leans itself ideally to such an approach. The acute care facility, for example, would be used in phase one. The alcoholic would be detoxified and stablized physically during the first seventy-two hours. Following, and, as much as possible, during detox, he would be exposed to an educational program of increasing intensity. Treatment during this phase would be geared primarily toward those needs identified within chapter three. After two weeks of intense education and treatment, the alcoholic would be transferred to a halfway house setting.

At the halfway house, phase one treatment would continue exactly where the acute care facility left off. Absolute communications are essential, of course, between all treatment sites. Upon completion of phase one, the recovering alcoholic would experience phase two treatment within the house. He would experience a controlled atmosphere while going to work daily from the house, returning thereto, and spending his weekends at home. His therapy would continue following the guidelines presented within chapter three. He would then be referred back to his primary counselor. Phase three would then be implemented and his rehabilitation plan, including aftercare, completed. The primary counselor, of course, would follow the alcoholic's treatment from beginning to end and be the ultimate responsible professional person.

Personally, I am in favor of some middle ground between expensive acute care facilities and halfway houses. It has been my contention for some time that insurance companies can not afford the higher treatment bills when relapse is so prevalent among alcoholics. It is not unusual, for example, for an alcoholic to have been in **treatment** two, three or four times. Unfortunately, many of these alcoholics are seeking help again when I see them. In addition, the private citizen is no longer willing, or able, to bear such expense when reward is so small. Therefore, social monies are *drying* up and programs are being cancelled. We can be better prepared for the inevitable by utilizing more halfway houses and staffing them only with essential personnel.

Another aspect of this waste is that treatment in the more "fancy" acute care facility is available to insured alcoholics only. Having worked in this setting for four years, my information is firsthand. I have seen many an alcoholic or drug addict turned away because he or she did not have insurance or cash money for treatment. Often, these alcoholics were more motivated toward recovery than the insured client. Many times, the insured client is coming in to treatment in order to save his job or in lieu of going to jail. While in treatment, these people often receive ninety percent of their normal pay every week. We need the alcoholic to be more responsible for his recovery than this. Self-help in conjunction with good counseling might be the only answer.

In concluding this final chapter of *About Alcoholism: A Common Sense Perspective,* I quote one of my favorite philosophers. Although, not experiencing alcoholism of epidemic proportions as we are today, his profound statement could be used as a guiding light for recovering persons of alcoholism everywhere.

> "By imagination and reason, we turn experience in to foresight. We become predictors of our future and cease to be slaves of our past." (Spinoza)

EPILOGUE

Alcoholism is probably the oldest infirmity brought onto ourselves through our own devices. It is here to stay and will have peaks and valleys in rate of incidence. I think we are at an all time peak right now with my estimate of twenty million direct sufferers within the United States alone. This statement is made with the knowledge of "statistical studies" still projecting a mere ten or twelve million. That's hogwash. Twenty years ago they were saying the same thing. In view of this "ostrich" syndrome, I still believe we are at a peak understanding and acceptance of this disease. That's great! However, we need to ensure understanding at all possible levels. This book was written toward accomplishing that goal.

It was written in a plain and common sense language as could only be done by an alcoholic. There have been books on alcoholism before this and will be after it is published. But there will never be another written by an author with so global a background on the subject and capability of sharing this experience with others. I believe we all have a goal in life to add some small contribution to the benefit of mankind. Some of us are fortunate enough to not only realize what that contribution is to be but also, through God's grace, given the experience and tools to reach its fulfillment. It is my desire that readers of this book receive at least one-tenth of benefit from this book as the author intended. If so, it will have accomplished my contribution. I can still see the look in my mother's eyes when she attempted to understand the complicated version of my theories as presented within my doctoral dissertation. She said, "Son, one of these days you will write a book which will help alcoholics. It will help them more than anything ever written." This book is dedicated to her. My grief is unexplainable that she didn't live to read it. But that is God's will.

GLOSSARY

AA: Alcoholics Anonymous. A self-help group for alcoholics. The only criteria for membership is a desire to stay sober.

Alanon: A self-help group for significant others of alcoholism. The only requirement for membership is a desire to get well and remain so.

Alateen: A self-help group similar to Alanon specifically for teen-aged significant others.

Alatot: A self-help group similar to Alanon specifically for significant others below the age of thirteen.

Alcoholism: A deteriorated state of living encompassing all within close proximity of an alcoholic.

Alter-ego: The person that one would like to be.

Antabuse: Generic name for Disulfiram. A medication without mood altering properties. It mixes quite violently with alcohol rendering one incapable of drinking while under its influence. Antabuse is effective in controlling compulsive drinking because once taken correctly, requires approximately five days for the organism to be rid of its influence.

Ativan: An addictive mood altering chemical.

Blackout: A phenomenon of alcoholism in which one maintains an outward semblance of consciousness, but in fact, unconscious as to memory. It can last hours or days. One can complete complicated tasks such as playing chess or driving while in a blackout. Blackouts are a definite sign of serious alcoholism progression and should not be taken lightly. This should not be confused with passing out which is when one goes to sleep and is physically inactive because of too much depressant (alcohol).

Coffee Cup Counselor (CCC): One who is quick to give advice and tell another what to do about his marriage, job, children, etc. This person is found at AA or Alanon meetings, has little or no counseling educational background. He is not to be confused with the helpful AA member or sponsor who shares with others what worked for him. An example of each are as follows. The CCC will say, "Here is what you should do with that husband. . . ." The helpful person, on the other hand, will say, "I did . . . and it worked for me." Avoid the CCC. His advice, although well-intentioned, might cause you more trouble in the long run.

Cold Turkey: Withdrawal from any addiction by abrupt cessation.

Contamination: Any emotion, especially anger, that has been suppressed into the Mt. St. Helen's inferno. The suppressed emotion attaches itself to other suppressed emotions thereby adding to its intensity or confusing its quality.

Detoxification: A timed process whereby the body rids itself of toxic chemicals. This process takes place primarily within the liver for ethyl alcohol and at a rate of about one ounce of alcohol per hour. There is no way to speed up this process. Black coffee is certainly not a quick way to "sober up". It will only cause a more active drunk.

Developmental Gap: As a result of non-confrontation EPA and not working through EPA, one becomes retarded in one's social development. The gap is the age difference at time of first confrontation and present. If, for example, a sixteen year old confronted with EPA relative to dancing elects to use alcohol to avoid confrontation, he will not advance in that area. If the EPA is thus avoided until age twenty-six, he will have a developmental gap of ten years.

Disulfiram: see Antabuse.

Drunk-a-log: A person who dwells on his actual drinking episodes while giving an AA lead. This is in conflict with AA format of telling how it was before alcohol, during alcohol and after AA came into his life. Drunk-a-log's are easy to fall in to, especially for the person giving his first lead.

Dry Drunk: A description of behavior which closely resembles that of a drinking person even though they are sober. This phenomenon occurs in the early stages of recovery and is identified by irritability, rigidness, anger and generalized unhappiness. It can last for days, weeks, months or even years. Dry drunk is a negative term in my estimation and if used, needs thorough explanation so as not to confuse the recovering alcoholic.

Ego: In Freudian psychology the ego is that part of our being which controls our daily living. It is our self-image, confidence, feelings of right and wrong with subsequent emotions and generally what we mean when we say "I". According to Freud, the ego is in conflict with a part of us (the Id) that wants immediate sexual gratification and that part of us which has the social do's, don'ts and should's (the Super Ego). The ego can be seen as the "mental brakes" mentioned in chapter one.

Enable: I do not use this term any longer and have replaced it with the term "support". It is defined as any behavior of a significant other that comes between the alcoholic and the full realization of any negative aspect of his drinking. For further definition of this term, please see "support system" within this glossary.

Halfway House: An organized, controlled refuge where alcoholics can recover. It is not a flop house where alcoholics lay drunk. There is normally a strong AA component within a halfway house and all residents are working on recovery. The halfway house is usually free standing, provides excellent recovery opportunity, is operated by recovering alcoholics with minimal staff. Costs are a fraction of the acute care hospital unit expenses.

Intervention: This is a planned, organized and rehearsed effort by counselor and family members to help the alcoholic recognize his disease. Ideally, the intervention is done in the alcoholic's home. Each participant reads a statement of observed behavior based on fact and prefaced by "Mom, I love you, am concerned about you and share this for your benefit. Last month you promised to attend my birthday party. You didn't because you were in bed with one of your 'sick' headaches. Actually, you were drunk." After everyone within the family shares similar observations, it is hoped the alcoholic will recognize their problem and agree to treatment. This is all orchestrated by a counselor who is ready with help if the intervention works.

Lead: The guest speaker at an AA meeting. He talks about his life before alcohol, during alcohol and after AA came into his life.

Librium: see Ativan.

Loss of Control: A sign of alcoholism. One might have intentions of drinking only one or two beers or mixed drinks and actually drink many more. There is always an excuse for this, but the bottom line is that the control of alcohol intake is lost.

Mellaril: see Ativan.

Miltown: see Ativan.

Mt. St. Helen's Syndrome: A graphic depiction of the need to recognize, verbalize and release emotions. Correct recognition is essential to all else relative to this theory. Basically, if these three steps are not taken, an explosive outlet will occur not too unlike the one felt in Washington State when the volcano Mt. St. Helen's erupted in 1981.

Mood Altering Chemical: A substance that causes the artificial changing of a mood or emotion without working through it normally.

Nervous Anxiety: An internal psychological disturbance in the form of an ungrounded fear that causes outward signs of fear. Anxiety can be so intense that one is paralyzed or very uncomfortable to the extent of being non-productive. Signs are sweaty palms, heart palpitations, shakiness, weak knees and the urge to run.

Paranoid: An intense fear that people or things are plotting against one. This can be extended to include the fear of being watched, followed, controlled, etc.

Psycho/Social Deprivation: Inability to fit into a given social setting due to experiencing more than a normal degree of uncomfortableness. The person so deprived is also seen as developmentally retarded.

Psychotropic: See mood altering chemical. Also commonly referred to as tranquilizers.

Relapse: A regression to an earlier stage or phase of recovery. Can include a regression to any point on the recovery continuum including a return to drinking and beyond.

Schizophrenia: A split from reality. Always accompanied by hallucinations in which one will see or hear 'things' that are not present. Also, there will be a delusional system in which one may feel persecuted or grandiose.

Sedative: Any chemical that depresses the central nervous system. On the street, sedative type chemicals are usually referred to as downers.

Significant other: A person, other than the alcoholic, who suffers from the influence of alcoholism. Can be a relative, spouse, friend or neighbor.

Sobriety time: The length of time in days from one's last drink to present. If one has a relapse during recovery, all previous sobriety time is lost and new sobriety time begins accumulating with day one.

Sponsor: A person of quality sobriety with at least one year duration. He or she becomes a mentor for a new member coming into AA.

Stable: This is an acronym that stands for Sober Thinking, Alcohol-Behavior Link Eliminated. This simply means that one is no longer motivated or controlled by alcohol in any way.

Stimulant: Any chemical that stimulates the central nervous system. In street terminology, a stimulant is referred to as an upper or speed.

Subconscious: That component of our thinking processes that is unknown to us. The subconscious can be thought of as the part of an iceberg below the water. It makes up a tremendously larger part of the overall mass than that seen. The subconscious mind causes us to behave in ways that we do not understand at the conscious level.

Support System: Visualize a close circle of people with outstretched hands all pushing with equal force upon an individual in the center. Imagine that the person in the middle is trying to fall, but can't because of the support of those surrounding him. Finally, as one person gets tired and leaves the circle, the others fill in the gap while maintaining an equal pressure. The center person, of course, is the alcoholic. He is sick, tired and really wants to fall, but the supporters won't allow it. They support by loaning him money, getting him out of trouble and making excuses. After the alcoholic's complete support system ceases to hold him up, he falls and begins to get well.

Thorazine: See Ativan.

Twelve Steps: A step by step process within AA whereby one can go from drinking to wellness. The steps should be followed in order, i.e., one, two, three, etc.

Unstable: An acronym that stands for Unhappy, Nervous, Sick-Thinking, Alcohol-Behavior Link Evident. Very simply, this means that one's motivation and behavior is oriented to alcohol. He or she is never physically free of the chemical long enough to allow the organism to stabilize.

APPENDIX

ALCOHOL-BLOOD-CHART

Showing estimated percentage of alcohol in the blood
by number of drinks in relation to body weight

Drinks ~	1	2	3	4	5	6	7	8	9	10	11	12
100 lbs.	.038	.075	.113	.150	.188	.225	.263	.300	.338	.375	.413	.450
120 lbs.	.031	.063	.094	.125	.156	.188	.219	.250	.281	.313	.344	.375
140 lbs.	.027	.054	.080	.107	.134	.161	.188	.214	.241	.268	.295	.321
160 lbs.	.023	.047	.070	.094	.117	.141	.164	.188	.211	.234	.258	.281
180 lbs.	.021	.042	.063	.083	.104	.125	.146	.167	.188	.208	.229	.250
200 lbs.	.019	.038	.056	.075	.094	.113	.131	.150	.169	.188	.206	.225
220 lbs.	.017	.034	.051	.068	.085	.102	.119	.136	.153	.170	.188	.205
240 lbs.	.016	.031	.047	.063	.078	.094	.109	.125	.141	.156	.172	.188

(Body Weight ~)

Has alcohol affected your driving ability?

~ This can be determined by the percentage of alcohol in your
blood. You can estimate your blood-alcohol level by
counting your drinks. (1 drink equals 1 volume oz. of 100
proof whiskey or 1-12 oz. bottle of beer.)
~ Use alcohol chart shown above ~ and under number of drinks
and opposite your body weight find the % of blood alcohol.
~ Subtract from this number the % of alcohol "burned up"
during the time elapsed since your first drink.

Hours since 1st drink   1   2   3   4   5   6
Subtract   .015% .030 .045 .060 .075 .090
The remainder is an estimate of the % of alcohol in your blood.
Example: 160 lb. man, 8 drinks, 6 hrs.
.188% − .090% = .098%

Interpretation of Results

% of blood-alcohol	Intoxicated?	If you drive a car ~
.000 to .050	No	Take it easy
.050 to .100	Maybe	Use extreme caution
.100 to	Yes	Don't !! You've had it !!

For best results - Don't drink and drive

EPA REDUCTION-NORMAL

EXPERIENTIAL
PRIMAL ANXIETY
(E.P.A.)

Based on a
scale of 1-7

Age of first experience

Experience (Dance)————————————————————— E.P.A. 7

E.P.A. viewed as normal

Continued experience ——————————————————— E.P.A. 7

Same experience repeated ——————————————
E.P.A. 6
E.P.A. 5
E.P.A. 4

As experience is repeated E.P.A. level will
diminish. Slight anxiety is normal, usually
E.P.A. 1-2.

There is *normal* development. Person is able to experience dancing
with a progressively reduced level of E.P.A. because of E.P.A. confrontation without alcohol or other mood altering chemical. **No developmental gap**.

(Continued on next page)

EPA REDUCTION-ABNORMAL

EXPERIENTIAL
PRIMAL ANXIETY
(E.P.A.)

Based on a
scale of 1-7

Age of first experience

Experience (Dance) ——————————————— E.P.A. 7

E.P.A. viewed as abnormal

Avoids experience (alcohol escape) ——————— E.P.A. -0-

Confronts same experience ——————————— E.P.A. 7

Avoids (stronger alcohol connection) ——————— E.P.A. -0-

Same type experience ———————————— E.P.A. 7

Avoids (alcoholism established) ——————————— E.P.A. -0-

Either accidentally or planned, a connection between EPA reduction and alcohol is made. This results in a temporary non-natural reduction of EPA. EPA will be present, however, at high levels of intensity on next and subsequent confrontations with the experience. Avoidance of this EPA through alcohol then becomes routine. Through association, the individual attempts to use alcohol-anxiety-reduction for all EPA arousing events. Therefore, alcoholism. **Developmental gap occurs** from time of first usage of alcohol to reduce EPA (anxiety). (See Chapter Two, Page 45) (Staccia, 1981)

PLEASURE CENTER

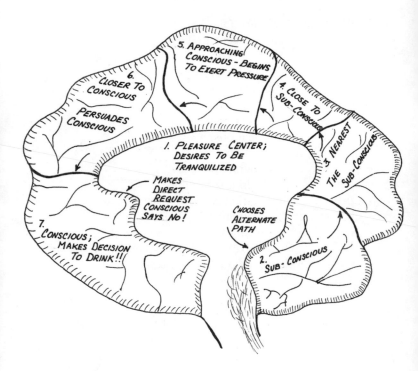

1) Pleasure center makes a direct request for alcohol. Conscious brain refuses because it is aware that alcohol has caused damage to the organism.

2) Pleasure center then seeks help from sub-conscious. Sub-conscious responds by creating problems.

3-5) As message reaches higher levels of consciousness, scenerio of problem solving centers on alcohol.

6) Pre-conscious then convinces conscious brain that without alcohol something horrible will happen, such as going crazy, having a nervous breakdown, unable to function, etc.

7) Conscious takes drink. (Staccia, 1981)

(See chapter three, page 56)

SOBRIETY CONTRACT

In order to remain free from all mood altering chemicals (MAC) and especially _____, I _____, will adhere to the following:

1. I will neither drink alcoholic beverages of any kind nor will I use any other MAC drug except under the strict supervision of a physician who is knowledgeable in the field of chemical dependency and aware of my particular history of addiction;

2. I will not allow alcohol or other MAC drugs to be brought into a house where I am the man/woman of the house;

3. I will not associate on a regular basis (more than required to perform certain social obligations) with anyone who is a using alcoholic or drug addict;

4. I will enter into a program of recovery which will include any treatment necessary to begin a sober lifestyle as prescribed by one who is a qualified rehabilitation counselor. I understand that such a program might include inpatient hospitalization;

5. I will, through my desire not to drink, join the fellowship of Alcoholics Anonymous and/or Narcotics Anonymous.

6. I will select a person of quality sobriety to sponsor me in the fellowship of AA/NA as soon as possible.

7. I will attend AA/NA meetings at least ____ times per week for three months and continue thereafter with at least ____ meetings for the next three months. After this initial six month period, my scheduled meetings will be self-adjusted while keeping in mind that the principles of AA/NA are my daily sobriety staple.

Signed _____Witnessed _____

The above contract was agreed to and   _____
signed on this date _____ 19 __.   _____
(see chapter three, page 57)

DEFENSIVE WALL ONE

The alcoholic shields his true emotions from self and others by building a wall. The wall is comprised of false emotions, dishonesty and phony portrayal of self to others. Those closest to the alcoholic react to this deceit by building similar walls. When these walls are in place, a very superficial and phony relationship exists between all.

(continued on next page)

DEFENSIVE WALL TWO

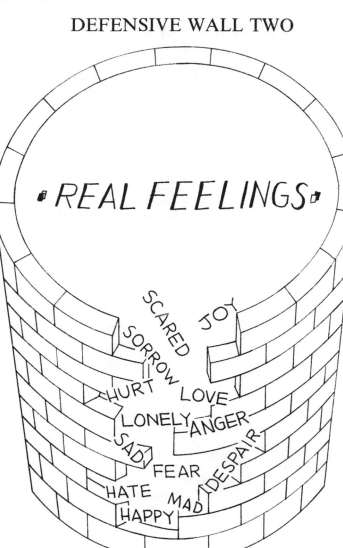

Through abstinence and rehabilitation efforts, the alcoholic's wall can be penetrated. This allows real feelings to pour out and he becomes real and vulnerable. It is important that similar thereapy be done with the significant others to insure against recontamination. As a result of this therapy, the alcoholic and his significant others return to an honest, loving, caring and real relationship. (Staccia, 1982)

(see chapter three, page 59)

MT. ST. HELEN'S SYNDROME ONE

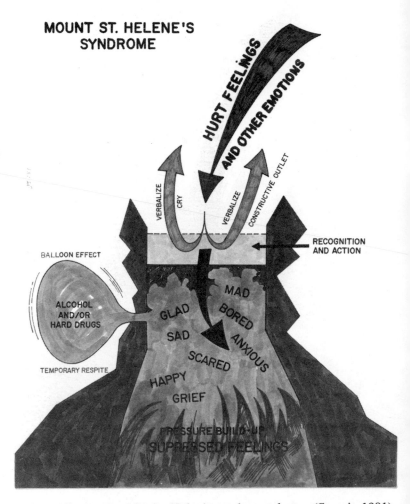

According to the Mt. St. Helen's syndrome theory (Staccia 1981), we are continually being bombarded with emotionally-laden stimuli. In order not to have difficulty with these emotions, we must do three things. First, we must recognize the stimulus relative to the type of emotion it arouses, e.g., love, hate, fear, etc. Secondly, we must act on this emotion by verbalizing it. Finally, we must take constructive physical action, i.e., talking about it, jogging, racquetball, walking, etc. As depicted, the alcoholic will invariably get drunk when experiencing emotional difficulties which offers only temporary respite.

(continued on next page)

MT. ST. HELEN'S SYNDROME TWO

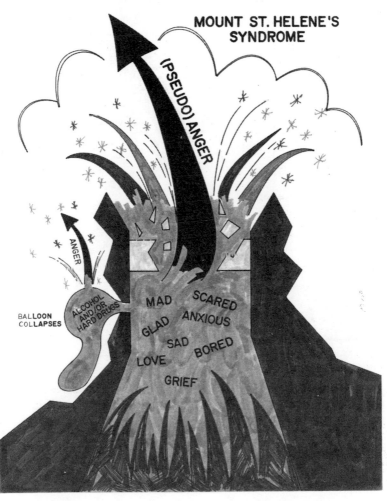

If conditions are not met exactly as described on the preceding page, then the emotion is suppressed into a seething volcanic-like pressure cooker. There, it is intertwined with other suppressed emotions and looses its identity. Occasionally, the suppressed emotion will attempt expression but is met with resistance from a crust created and thickened through time. It is then deflected back into the cauldron where pressure continues to build. Eventually, the pressure becomes overwhelming and an explosion of pseudo-anger occurs, usually directed at an innocent third party.

(see chapter three, page 61)

MMPI PROFILE ONE

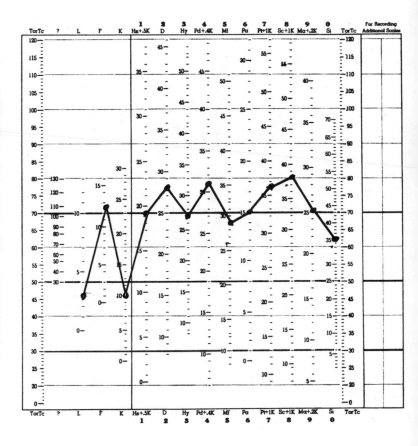

Depicted on this graph from the Minnesota Multiphasic Personality Inventory (MMPI) is a composite profile of forty-seven alcoholics. There have been only six or less days elapsed since their last drink. Notice the elevated peaks on just about every personality characteristic measured. (Staccia, 1983)

(continued on next page)

MMPI PROFILE TWO

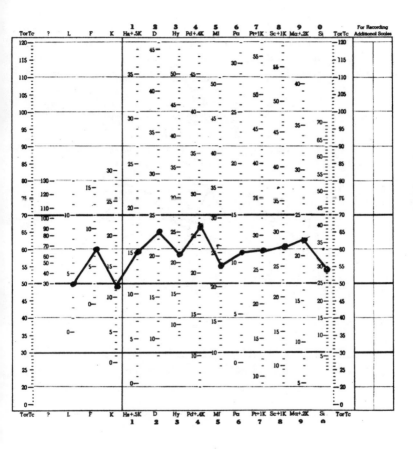

This MMPI graph depicts another composite profile of alcoholics. Notice that the peaks are all within normal range. Interestingly, the only "treatment" received of this population was chemical dissipation from the organism and routine rehabilitation counseling. (Staccia, 1983)

(see chapter three, page 70)

SUBJECTIVE ANXIETY MEASUREMENT SCALE (SAMS)

The following scenarios present situations which might arouse anxious reactions (i.e., sweaty palms, rapid heartbeat, shallow breathing, desire to avoid the situation) in an individual. Mark the degree to which you would react in such an anxious manner in each (1 indicates little to no reaction and 7 indicates strong reaction). Mark by circling number.

1. You are going to meet your girlfriend's/boyfriend's parents for the first time.

$$1 \quad 2 \quad 3 \quad 4 \quad 5 \quad 6 \quad 7$$

2. You are about to be interviewed for a new job.

$$1 \quad 2 \quad 3 \quad 4 \quad 5 \quad 6 \quad 7$$

3. The report requested of you is due tomorrow and you don't think you will have enough time to finish it.

$$1 \quad 2 \quad 3 \quad 4 \quad 5 \quad 6 \quad 7$$

4. Initiation into a lodge/club requires you to sing the National Anthem.

$$1 \quad 2 \quad 3 \quad 4 \quad 5 \quad 6 \quad 7$$

5. You are going to a party where there will be dancing. Your date/spouse will coax you onto the floor.

$$1 \quad 2 \quad 3 \quad 4 \quad 5 \quad 6 \quad 7$$

6. For the first time in your life you have been selected to address a large group of people concerning opinions on an issue.

$$1 \quad 2 \quad 3 \quad 4 \quad 5 \quad 6 \quad 7$$

7. You are on your way to a doctor's office for a complete physical exam.

$$1 \quad 2 \quad 3 \quad 4 \quad 5 \quad 6 \quad 7$$

8. You are at work/school when you receive a message to call home as soon as possible.

$$1 \quad 2 \quad 3 \quad 4 \quad 5 \quad 6 \quad 7$$

9. You have been notified to contact your advisor/supervisor as soon as possible to discuss the quality of your work.

$$1 \quad 2 \quad 3 \quad 4 \quad 5 \quad 6 \quad 7$$

10. You are taking an examination for promotion in the near future and you were unable to review all the material that will be covered.

$$1 \quad 2 \quad 3 \quad 4 \quad 5 \quad 6 \quad 7$$

The Subjective Anxiety Measurement Scale (SAMS) is an instrument to measure one's perceived anxiety. The differential between perceived and real anxiety can be a contributing factor in alcoholism causation. The SAMS is also an excellent counseling aid as an instrument of prevention because of its effectiveness in predicting one's alcoholism propensity.

(see chapter 3, page 71)

RELAPSE WARNING GUIDE

We are all one drink away from a drunk, as the saying goes. Relapse is certainly possible for the recovering alcoholic and is practically a foregone conclusion if we do not take steps to prevent it. The following method of avoiding relapse is based on common sense and recognition of behavior. Shared below are a few examples of things to avoid. Of course, there are many more. Every recovering alcoholic knows what "things" he needs to avoid. If one is not avoiding these things and especially if they are actively becoming involved in them, relapse is imminent.

(1) Do not confine yourself to home. Get out and enjoy life. On the other hand, old habits must be broken. (2) Do not go fishing with the "boys" if they are old drinking buddies who take more alcoholic beverage than bait on the trip. (3) Do not stop by Tony's Tavern to have a Pepsi with the boys. (4) Do not overwork. (5) Do not be rigid and disagreeable with spouse and family. (6) Do not avoid the spiritual aspect of recovery (7) If you engage excessively in any or all of these activities, you will drink.

In addition to being aware of the above, you might make an "alternative to drink" list (Staccia, 1982). It is simply a list of prioritized alternatives to avoid taking a drink when the urge or compulsion to drink hits you. If the list is long enough, and you follow it honestly, you should be safe.

1. Talk with spouse and family.
2. Call your sponsor.
3. Call a friend.
4. Take a walk.
5. Go jogging.
6. Read a book.
7. Go to a movie.
8. Go to church/synagogue
9. Call your minister/rabbi
10. Play some physical sport.
11. Go shopping.
12. Take a drive in the country.
13. Etc . . . . . .

(see chapter three page 77)

ALCOHOL INFLUENCE OVER TIME

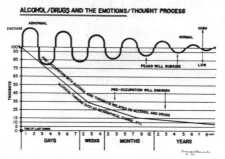

This chart depicts the emotional and cognitive aspects of recovery and how they react over time. Notice a 100% contamination of alcohol on the brain and emotions from the first day of sobriety, a dramatic reduction of this influence the first week, and then a more gradual reduction after that. This contamination is seen as a pre-occupation with drinking and the classic thoughts of a "geographical change". Also, the emotions are "swinging" radically with large gaps between feelings of happy and sad.

ACUTE EFFECTS OF
ALCOHOL ON BRAIN

Anesthetic Effect of Alcohol
The Intelligent Capacity
1. Care and anxiety diminished
1. Reaction time slowed
2. Thinking disturbed
1. Self-control released
1. Judgment impaired
1. Inhibitions released

Motor & Sensory Control
2. Stuttering and stammering
2. Staggering
2. Seeing double
2. Distorted hearing
2. Disturbed Equilibrium

Unlearned Activities
5. Falls into stupor
4. Unable to hear
4. Unable to move.
5. Blood circulation stops
5. Breathing stops

Effects of alcohol work
downward

Effects of Alcohol
on the brain
and nervous system

Normal Activities
Highest Level of Intelligence
2. Self-Criticism
1. Self-Control
1. Judgment
1. Reasoning
1. Discrimination
1. Sense of right and wrong

Learned Activities
2. Talking
2. Singing
2. Writing
3. Walking
2. Riding a bicycle, skating, etc.

Activities Performed at Birth
4. Crying
4. Movement
5. Breathing
4. Taking food
5. Blood Circulation.

The human brain develops
upward

Legend
1. Frontal Lobe – Cerebrum
2. Parietal Lobe – Cerebrum
3. Occipital Lobe – Cerebrum
4. Cerebellum
5. Thalamus and Medulla

PG 156 Bum Sides

This is a self-explanatory chart showing the acute influence that alcohol has over the mind. It is interesting to note that we strive for intellectual maturity from birth and then lose it almost with the very first drink.

MOOD ALTERING CHEMICAL
UMBRELLA (MAC)

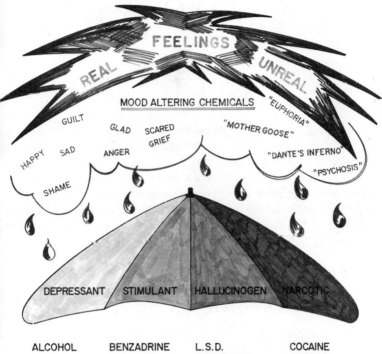

DEPRESSANT	STIMULANT	HALLUCINOGEN	NARCOTIC
ALCOHOL	BENZADRINE	L.S.D.	COCAINE
VALIUM	DESOXYN	MARIJUANA	CODEINE
BENADRYL	DEXADRINE	MESCALINE	DARVON
HALDOL	METHADRINE	P.C.P.	DEMEROL
LIBRIUM	RITALIN	METHAQUALONE	DILAUDID
THORAZINE	CAFFEINE	(PEYOTE)	HASHISH
QUAALUDE	DEXAMYL	GLUE	METHADONE
MILTOWN	DESBUTAC	TOLUENE	HEROIN

The MAC Umbrella depicts four categories of Mood Altering Chemicals (MAC). Each category in turn is represented by several chemicals. The list is far from inclusive and its popularity changes almost daily. Basically if one is addicted to any drug under the umbrella, one is subject to addiction from them all.

About Alcoholism: A Common Sense Perspective is the first in a series of common sense perspective books to be released by Acosep Corporation, Publishing Division. Planned publications include but are not limited to the following:

Anxiety: A Common Sense Perspective
Choosing A Career: A Common Sense Perspective
Counseling: A Common Sense Perspective
Marriage: A Common Sense Perspective
Parenting: A Common Sense Perspective
Terminal Illness: A Common Sense Perspective